117 PRACTICAL
IC PROJECTS
YOU CAN BUILD

No. 2645
$16.95

117 PRACTICAL
IC PROJECTS
YOU CAN BUILD

R.H. WARRING AND
DELTON T. HORN

TAB BOOKS Inc.

Blue Ridge Summit, PA 17214

FIRST EDITION

FIRST PRINTING

Copyright © 1986 by TAB BOOKS Inc.

Printed in the United States of America

Library of Congress Cataloging in Publication Data

Warring, R. H. (Ronald Horace), 1920—1984
    117 practical IC projects you can build.

    Rev. ed. of: 84 practical IC projects you can
build. c1979.
    Includes index.
    1. Integrated circuits—Amateurs' manuals.
I. Horn, Delton T. II. Warring, R. H. (Ronald Horace),
1920-1984. 84 practical IC projects you can build.
III. Title.   IV. Title: One hundred seventeen practical
IC projects you can build.
TK9966.W37 1986   621.381′73   86-5975
ISBN 0-8306-0445-6
ISBN 0-8306-2645-X (pbk.)

Contents

List of Working Circuits

Introduction

Integrated Circuits (or ICs) are the building blocks from which modern electronic circuits are assembled. They save a lot of time in construction and give better performance than similar circuits built from separate components and, above all, are incredibly space saving. In these respects they are a big step ahead of single transistors and have made it easier for amateur constructors—as well as professionals—to build working circuits.

There are thousands of different types of ICs, each of which may be adaptable to many different working circuits (although some of the more complex ones are designed with a limited range of application). This can be quite bewildering, especially knowing how and where to start. However, from the point of view of using ICs and putting them to work, there is no need at all to know the actual circuits they contain—merely what type of circuit they contain and how their leads or pins are connected to other components to complete a working circuit.

That is what this book is about. It explains and "classifies" integrated circuits in simple terms. It covers the various ways in which the simplest ICs—op-amps—can be worked and describes a whole range of working circuits based on selected—and inexpensive—integrated circuits.

In this revised edition, several new projects have been added, some using recently developed ICs. All in all, this volume features 117 different working projects you can build.

In fact it is really a basic—and essentially practical—"course" on understanding and using integrated circuits.

Chapter 1

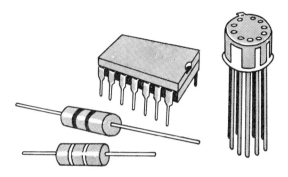

The Basics of Integrated Circuits

The transistor first appeared as a working device in 1947, since which time it has been manufactured in hundreds of millions. It took a little time to realize that the same techniques used for producing individual transistors could be applied to complete circuits and sub-circuits containing both active components (e.g., diodes and transistors) and passive components (e.g., resistors and capacitors), with all necessary interconnections in a single unit familiarly known as a "chip."

Apart from the obvious advantage of being able to produce complete circuits and sub-circuits in this way, the cost of producing a complex circuit by photo-etching techniques is little more than that of producing individual transistors, and the bulk of the circuit can be reduced substantially since transistors in integrated circuits do not need encapsulation or canning, and resistors and capacitors do not need "bodies." Another advantage is the potentially greater reliability offered by integrated circuits, since all components are fabricated simultaneously and there are no soldered joints. (Performance can also be improved as more complex circuits can be used where advantageous at little or no extra cost.

The next big step in integrated circuit construction was the development of microelectronic technology or extreme miniaturization of such components and integrated circuits. Photo-etching is readily suited to this, the main problem being in checking individual components for faults due to imperfections in the manufacturing process, and achieving a high yield of fault-free chips per "wafer" manufactured. Rejection rates are liable to rise with increasing complexity of the circuit, but modern processes now achieve a very high yield.

Basically, an integrated circuit consists of a single chip of silicon, typically about 1.25 mm square (0.050 inches square) in size. Each chip may contain 50 or more separate components, all interconnected (although they may contain very many less for simpler circuits). The actual manufacturing process is concerned with producing wafers, each of which may contain several hundred chips. These wafers are processed in batches, so one single batch production may be capable of producing several thousand integrated circuit chips simultaneously, involving a total of tens of thousands of components.

It is this high production yield which is responsible for the relatively low price of integrated circuits—usually substantially less than the cost of the equivalent individual components in a chip produced separately, and in the case of some chips even less than that of a single transistor. The final selling price, however, is largely governed by demand. The integrated circuit is a mass-production item and the greater the demand for a particular chip, the lower the price at which it can be sold economically.

Figure 1-1 shows a typical—and fairly simple—IC produced as a flat "package" encapsulated in plastic. The drawing is approximately 1 1/2 times actual size (9.4 mm long by 6 mm wide). Figure 1-2 shows the complete circuit contained in this IC, comprising 16 transistors, 8 diodes and 13 resistors. Figure 1-3 shows the physical appearance of the chip, much magnified, when it is part of the wafer. The actual size of this chip is approximately 2.5 mm by 2 mm.

The actual *component density* or number of components per unit area, may vary considerably in integrated circuits. The figure of 50 components per chip has already been mentioned, which is

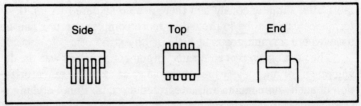

Fig. 1-1. Outline shape of a typical 8-pin dual-in-line integrated circuit, about 1 1/2 times actual size.

typical of small-scale integration (SSI). It is possible to achieve much higher component densities. With medium-scale integration (MSI), component density is greater than 100 components per chip; and with large-scale integration (LSI), component density may be as high as 1000 or more components per chip. Both MSI and LSI are extensions of the original integrated circuit techniques using similar manufacturing methods. The only difference is in the matter of size and physical separation of the individual components and the method of inter-connection.

MONOLITHIC AND HYBRID ICs

Integrated circuits where all the components and connections are formed in the substrate of the "chip" are known as *monolithic ICs*. There is a further class of ICs where the individual components (transistors, diodes, resistors, etc.), or even complete sub-circuits, are all attached to the same substrate but with intercon-

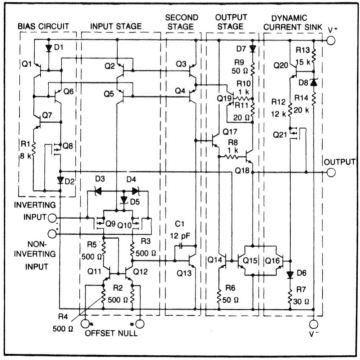

Fig. 1-2. Schematic diagram of one half of a CA3240 BiMOS operational amplifier showing components and interconnections all formed in the substrate of the chip.

3

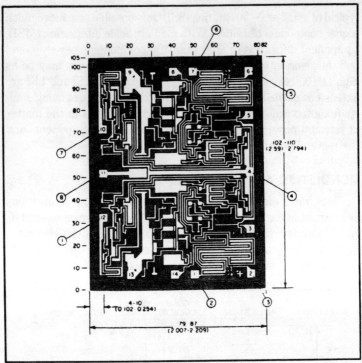

Fig. 1-3. Much enlarged illustration of the CA3240 chip containing two complete circuits like Fig. 1-2. Actual dimensions of this chip are 2.5 by 2 millimeters. Grid dimensions marked around the outside of the diagram are in thousandths of an inch.

nections formed by wire bonding. These are known as *hybrid ICs*. In hybrid circuits, electrical isolation is provided by the physical separation of the components.

IC COMPONENTS

Transistors and *diodes* are formed directly on the surface of the chip with their size and geometry governing their electrical characteristics as well as density level, etc. Where a number of such components are involved in a complete integrated circuit their performance is usually better than that of a circuit with discrete (separate) components because they are located close together and their electrical characteristics are closely matched.

Resistors can be formed by silicon resistance stripes etched in the slice, or by using the bulk resistivity of one of the diffused areas. There are limits, however, to both the range and tolerance of re-

4

sistance values which can be produced by these methods. "Stripe" resistors are limited to a minimum width of about 0.025 mm (0.001 in.) to achieve a tolerance of 10 percent. Practical values obtained from diffused resistors range from about 10 Ω to 30 KΩ, depending on the method of diffusion with tolerances of plus or minus 10 percent. Better performance can be achieved with thin-film resistors with resistance values ranging from 20 Ω to 50 KΩ.

A method of getting round this problem when a high resistance is required is to use a transistor biased almost to cut-off, instead of a resistor, in an integrated circuit where a resistance value of more than 50 KΩ is required. This is quite economic in the case of integrated circuit manufacture and is a method widely used in practice.

Capacitors present more of a problem. Small values of capacitance can be produced by suitable geometric spacing between circuit elements and utilizing the stray capacitance generated between these elements. Where rather higher capacitance values are required, individual capacitors may be formed by a reversed-bias PN junction; or as thin-film "plate" type using a tiny aluminum plate and a MOS (metal-oxide-semiconductor) second plate. The former method produces a *polarized* capacitor and the thin film method a *non-polarized* capacitor. The main limitation in either case is the relatively low limit to size and capacitance values which can be achieved—typically 0.2 pF per 0.025 mm (0.001 in.) square for a junction capacitor and up to twice this figure with a thin film MOS capacitor, both with fairly wide tolerances (plus or minus 20 percent). Where anything more than moderate capacitor values are needed in an integrated circuit it is usually the practice to omit the capacitor from the circuit and connect a suitable discrete component externally.

Both resistors and capacitors fabricated in ICs also suffer from high temperature coefficients (i.e., working values varying with temperature) and may also be sensitive to voltage variations in the circuit.

Unlike printed circuits, it is not possible to fabricate inductors or transformers in integrated circuits at the present state-of-the-art. As far as possible, therefore, ICs are designed without the need for such components; or where this is not possible, a separate conventional component is connected externally to the integrated circuit.

From the above it will be appreciated that integrated circuits are quite commonly used as "building blocks" in a complete circuit, connected to other conventional components. A simple example is shown in Fig. 1-4 using a ZN414 as a basic "building block" in the construction of a miniature AM radio. Although it is a high gain device (typical power gain 72 dB), the integrated circuit needs a following stage of transistor amplification to power a crystal earpiece; high value decoupling capacitors; and a standard coil and tuning capacitor for the tuned circuit. The complete circuit is capable of providing an output of 500 millivolts across the earpiece, with a supply voltage of 1.3 and typical current drain of 0.3 milliamps.

THE SHAPE OF ICs

ICs come in various "package" shapes. Quite a number have the same shape (and size) as a typical transistor and are only readily identified as an IC because of the greater number of leads emerging from the bottom (a transistor usually has only three leads). These shapes are defined by the standard coding adopted for transistor outlines, e.g., TO-5, TO-18, etc., which also identifies the individual pins by numbers (e.g., see Fig. 1-5D, E and F).

Other ICs come in the form of flat packages with leads emerging from each side. These are three different arrangements used (see Fig. 1-5A, B, C, and G).

- Dual in-line, where the leads on each side are bent down to form two separate rows to plug directly into a printed circuit panel or IC holder (A and B).
- Quad in-line, like dual in-line, except that the leads on each side form two parallel rows (G).
- Flat, where the leads emerge straight and from each side of the package (C).

In all cases leading numbering normally runs around the package, starting from top left and ending at top right (again see Fig. 1-5). The number of leads may be anything from eight to sixteen or even more.

Some types of holders designed to match standard pin configurations or flat shape ICs are shown in Fig. 1-6. These holders have pin configurations similar to the ICs they take. Their principal advantage is that they can be soldered to a printed circuit or Veroboard, etc., with no risk of heat damage to the IC itself since this is only plugged in after soldered connections are completed. Most circuit constructors, however, prefer to solder ICs directly to a printed circuit panel (or Veroboard).

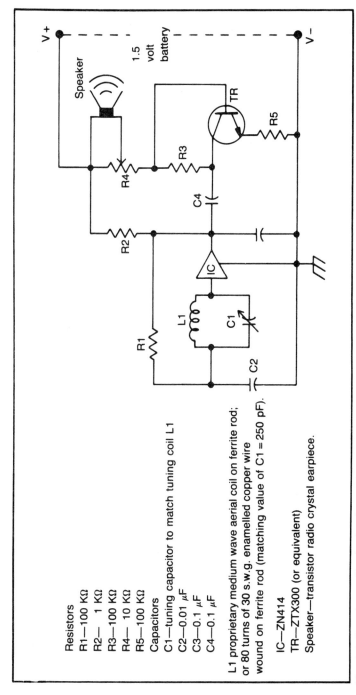

Resistors
R1—100 KΩ
R2— 1 KΩ
R3—100 KΩ
R4— 10 KΩ
R5—100 KΩ
Capacitors
C1—tuning capacitor to match tuning coil L1
C2—0.01 μF
C3—0.1 μF
C4—0.1 μF

L1 proprietary medium wave aerial coil on ferrite rod;
or 80 turns of 30 s.w.g. enamelled copper wire
wound on ferrite rod (matching value of C1 = 250 pF).

IC—ZN414
TR—ZTX300 (or equivalent)
Speaker—transistor radio crystal earpiece.

Fig. 1-4. Complete radio circuit using a ZN414 integrated circuit connected to external components.

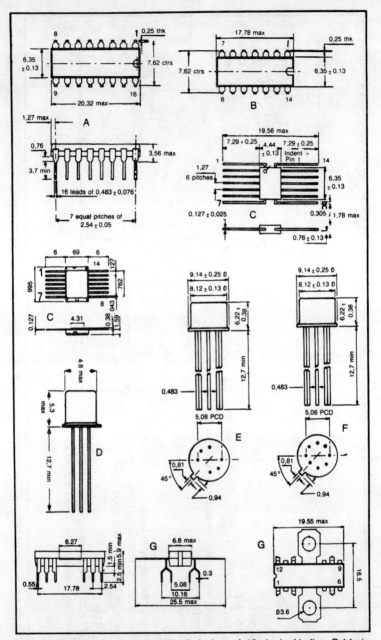

Fig. 1-5. Examples of integrated circuit designs. A 16-pin dual in-line. B 14-pin dual in-line. C flat (ceramic) package. D 3-lead transistor "can" shape. E 6-lead "transistor" shape. F 8-lead "transistor" shape. G 12-pin quad in-line with heat sink tabs.

8

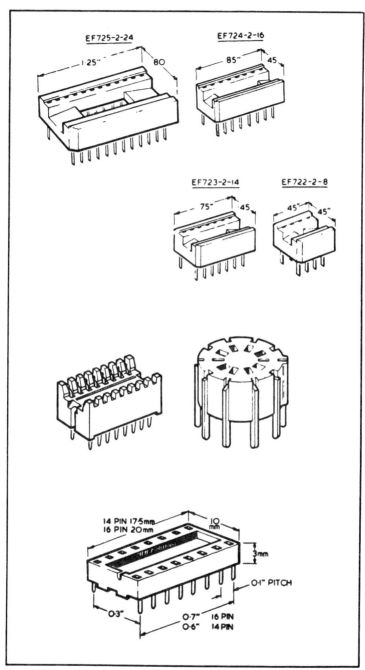

Fig. 1-6. Examples of integrated circuit holders (Electrovalue).

Chapter 2

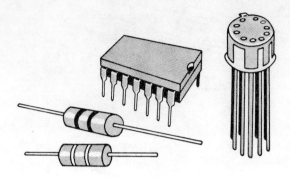

"General Purpose" ICs (Arrays)

The description "general purpose" is not accepted terminology but it is used here to describe integrated circuit chips which comprise a number of individual components, usually transistors and possibly also diodes, each component in the chip connecting to individual outlet leads. Thus by connecting to the appropriate leads an individual transistor (or diode) can be connected to an external circuit. Other chips of this type may also include components connected within the chip, e.g., transistors in Darlington pairs, but the same principle of application applies. The technical description of such a chip is an *integrated circuit array*.

A simple example of such a chip is shown in Fig. 2-1. It consists of three transistors (two interconnected); two types of diodes; and a zener diode. This particular chip is used in the voltage regulator circuit described in Chapter 8 (Fig. 8-4), using two of the transistors, the SCR diode and the zener diode.

This circuit design is shown in Fig. 2-2. The components to be utilized which are contained in the IC are enclosed in the dashed outline, i.e., TR1, TR2, D2 and D3. The other components in the chip (D1 and TR3) are not required. Resistors R1, R2, R3 and R4 and a capacitor C, are all discrete components connected externally.

Figure 2-3 re-examines the component disposition of the chip, together with the necessary external connections. Note that the arrangement of the leads or *pin-out* arrangement does not necessarily follow the schematic diagram (Fig. 2-1) where the pins are in

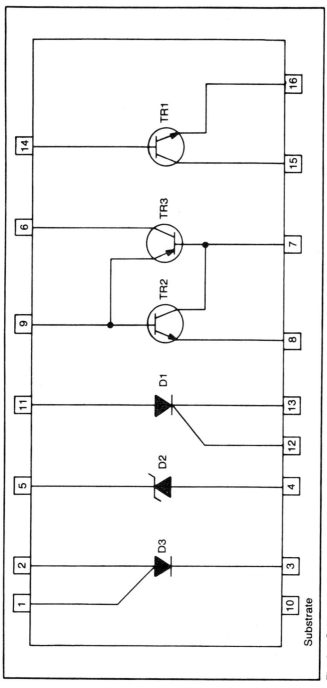

Fig. 2-1. Schematic diagram of CA3097E integrated circuit array which contains two diodes, one zener diode, two NPN transistors and one PNP transistor. Numbered pin connections are also shown, these provide access to individual components in the chip. These pins are not in the physical order as found on the chip (see Fig. 2-3).

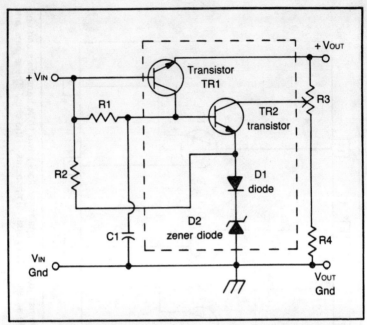

Fig. 2-2. Voltage regulator circuit. Components within the dashed outline are in the CA3097E integrated circuit. R1, R2, R3, R4 and C1 are external components.

random order to clarify connections to internal components. The actual pin-out arrangement on ICs follows a logical order reading around the chip. Schematic diagrams may or may not follow in the same order (usually not).

Connections for completing the circuit of Fig. 2-3 are:

Leads 1, 2 and 3 are ignored as D1 is not used.

Lead 4 connects one side of the zener diode to the common earth line and Lead 5 to Lead 13, connecting the zener diode to the correct side of the SCR (diode).

Now to pick up the transistor connections. The base of TR1 (15) connects to the external resistor R1; and the collector lead (14) to the other side of R1, which is also the input point for the circuit. The emitter lead (16) connects to output.

TR2 and TR3 in the chip are interconnected, but only one of these transistors is required. Connecting lead (6) to (9) shorts out TR2, which is not wanted. Connecting the emitter lead (8) of TR3 to 11-12 (already joined); the collector lead (9) to (6); and the base lead (7) to the center tag of the external potentiometer R3 connects TR3 into the circuit.

It only remains for the external component connections to be completed. These are:

R2 to lead (14) and lead (12).

Capacitor C to lead (6) and earth point. Lead (10) on the IC is also the substrate or earthing point of the IC, so should also be connected to the common earth line.

One end of the potentiometer R3 to the top (output) line.

The other end of the potentiometer R3 to R4.

The other end of R4 to the bottom common earth line.

SPARE COMPONENTS

A number of components in an array may not be used in a particular circuit, but the cost of the single IC can often be less than that of the equivalent transistors or diodes ordered separately and used individually to complete the same circuit. The circuit using the IC will also be more compact and generally easier to construct.

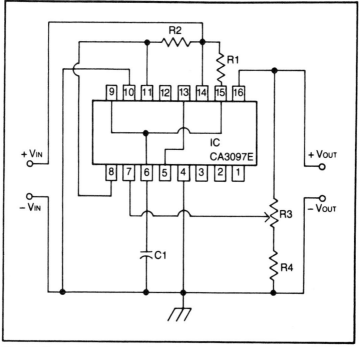

Fig. 2-3. Completed voltage regulator circuit showing wiring connections made to the integrated circuit. Pins in this diagram are shown in the actual physical order they appear on the integrated circuit. Note. For clarity the integrated circuit is drawn much larger in proportion to the external components.

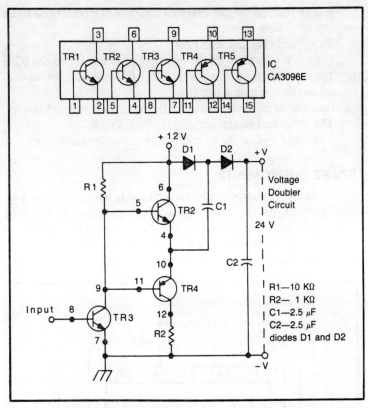

Fig. 2-4. Schematic diagram of CA array (top) and voltage doubler circuit using TR2, TR3 and TR4 from the array together with external components.

The spare transistors in the array (TR1 and TR5) can be used instead of separate diodes, connected for diode working by ignoring the collector leads.

A little study sometimes shows where further savings are possible. Figure 2-4, for example, shows a voltage doubler circuit for a 1 kHz square wave input signal, based on a CA3096E IC array which contains 5 transistors. Only three of these transistors are used in this particular circuit, leaving two "spare."

The circuit calls for two diodes D1 and D2 (as well as three resistors and two capacitors) to be added as discrete components. Transistors can also be worked as diodes (by neglecting the collector lead), and so the functions of D1 and D2 could be performed by the two "spare" transistors in the array (thus using up all its components).

Alternatively, since the current needs a square wave input signal, the two "spare" transistors could be used in a multivibrator

14

circuit to provide this input. Since diodes are cheaper than transistors, this is a more economic way of using all the components in the original array.

The fact that popular ICs are quite cheap means that it is seldom worth while going to elaborate methods of trying to use all the components available in an array, unless such utilization is fairly obvious, as above. Using only part of an array can still show savings over the purchase of individual components for many circuits.

The *astable multivibrator* circuit shown in Fig. 2-5, for example, only uses one of the three complete switching circuits contained in the CA3600E array, associated with an OTA CA3080 integrated circuit and four external resistors. On the other hand, Fig. 2-6 shows a high gain amplifier circuit using all the components in the CA3600E array with external resistors.

CONSTANT CURRENT CIRCUIT

A useful circuit employing the CA3018 integrated circuit array is shown in Fig. 2-7. This array comprises four transistors (two

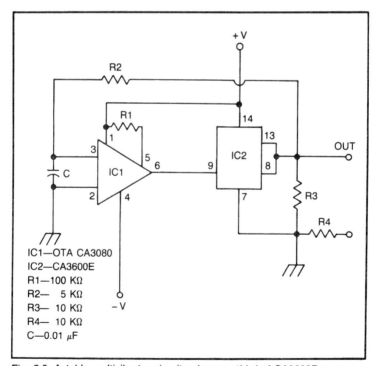

Fig. 2-5. Astable multivibrator circuit using one third of CA3600E array.

15

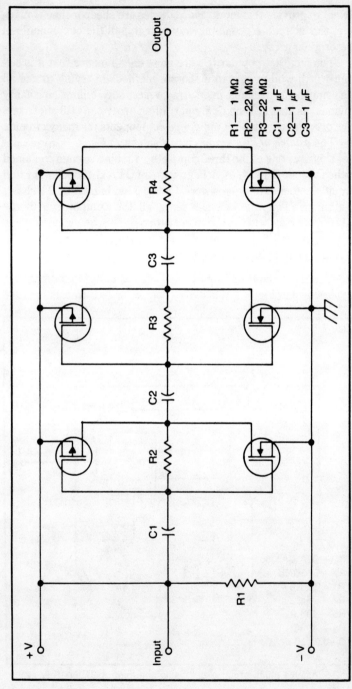

R1— 1 MΩ
R2—22 MΩ
R3—22 MΩ
C1—1 μF
C2—1 μF
C3—1 μF

Fig. 2-6. High-gain amplifier circuit using the complete CA3600E integrated circuit together with external components.

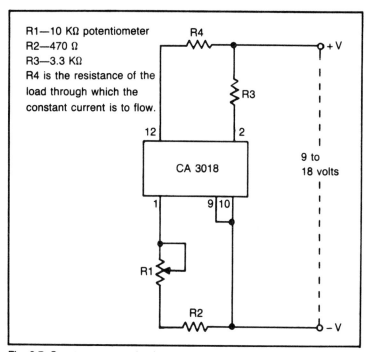

Fig. 2-7. Constant current circuit using components found in CA3018 array.

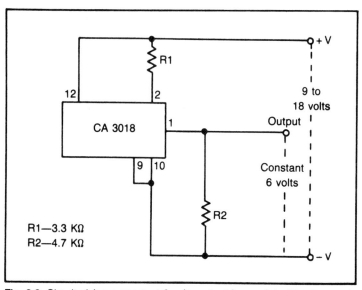

Fig. 2-8. Circuit giving a constant 6 volts output from a 9 to 18 volts supply voltage, again using the CA3018 array.

interconnected as a super-alpha pair) and four diodes. Tapping the super-alpha pair of transistors, a *constant current* source can be produced, the magnitude of this current being set by adjustment of the potentiometer R1 over a range of about 0.2 mA to 14 mA, depending on the actual supply voltage.

The same integrated circuit can also be used as a *constant voltage* source—Fig. 2-8. In this case the constant voltage output is the zener voltage of the transistor worked as a zener diode, which is approximately 6 volts.

Chapter 3

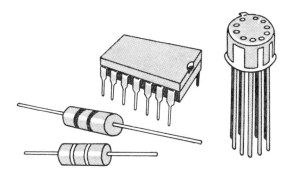

Op-Amps

Op-amps (operational amplifiers) are a particular class of integrated circuit comprising a directly-coupled high-gain amplifier with overall response characteristics controlled by feedback. The op-amp gets its name from the fact that it can be made to perform numerous mathematical operations. An op-amp is the basic building block in many analog systems and is also known as a *linear integrated circuit* because of its response.

It has an extremely high gain (theoretically approaching infinity), the actual value of which can be set by the feedback. The introduction of capacitors or inductors in the feedback network can give gain varying with frequency and thus determine the operating condition of the whole integrated circuit.

The basic op-amp is a three-terminal device with two inputs and one output—Fig. 3-1. The input terminals are described as "inverting" and "non-inverting." At the input there is a virtual "short circuit," although the feedback keeps the voltage across these points at zero so that no current flows across the "short." The simple circuit equivalent is also shown in Fig. 3-1, when the voltage gain is given by a ratio of the impedances Z2/Z1.

OP-AMP PARAMETERS

The ideal op-amp is perfectly balanced so that if fed with equal inputs, output is zero, i.e.

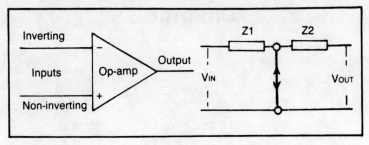

Fig. 3-1. A basic op-amp is a three terminal device with the corresponding circuit as shown.

$$V_{IN}\, 1\, =\, V_{IN}\, 2\ \text{gives}\ V_{OUT}\, =\, 0$$

In a practical op-amp the input is not perfectly balanced so that unequal bias currents flow through the input terminal. Thus an input offset voltage must be applied between the two input terminals to balance the amplifier output.

The *input bias current* (I_B) is one half the sum of the separate currents entering the two input terminals when the output is balanced, i.e., $V_{OUT} = 0$. It is usually a small value, e.g., a typical value is $I_B = 100$ nA.

The *input offset current* (I_{io}) is the difference between the separate currents entering the input terminals. Again it is usually of a very small order, e.g., a typical value is $I_{io} = 10$ nA.

The *input offset voltage* (V_{io}) is a voltage which must be applied across the input terminal, to balance the amplifier. Typical value, $V_{io} = 1$ mV.

Both I_{io} and V_{io} are subject to change with temperature, this change being known as I_{io} drift and V_{io} drift, respectively.

The *Power Supply Rejection Ratio* (PSRR) is the ratio of the change in input offset voltage to the corresponding change in one power supply voltage. Typically this is of the order of $10 - 20\ \mu V/V$.

Other parameters which may be quoted for op-amps are:
Open-loop gain—usually designated A_d.
Common-mode rejection ratio—designated CMRR. This is the ratio of the difference signal to the common-mode signal and represents a figure of merit for a differential amplifier. This ratio is expressed in decibels (dB).
Slew rate—or the rate of change of amplifier output voltage under large-signal conditions. It is expressed in terms of $V/\mu s$.

Some examples of the versatility of the op-amp are given in the following simple circuits:

AMPLIFIER OR BUFFER

Figure 3-2 shows the circuit for an inverting amplifier, or inverter. The gain is equal to:

$$Av = -R2/R1$$

Notice that if the two resistances are equal (i.e., R1 = R2), the gain is negative one, meaning that the circuit works as a phase inverting voltage follower. The output will be the same as the input, except the polarity will be reversed.

In fact, for unity gain, the resistors can be eliminated and replaced with direct connections, as illustrated in Fig. 3-3. This works because in this circuit R1 = R2 = 0. R3 is usually eliminated in the inverting voltage follower circuit.

If R1 is smaller than R2, the input signal will be amplified at the output. For example, if R1 is 2.2 KΩ and R1 is 22 KΩ, the gain will be:

$$Av = -22,000/2,200 = -10$$

The minus sign indicates phase inversion. The output polarity is reversed from the input.

The same circuit can also attenuate (reduce the level of) the input signal by making R1 larger than R2. For example, if R1 is 120 KΩ, and R2 is 47 KΩ, the circuit gain will be approximately:

$$Av = 47,000/120,000 = -0.4$$

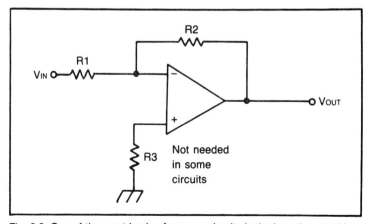

Fig. 3-2. One of the most basic of op-amp circuits is the inverting amplifier.

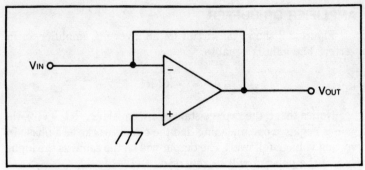

Fig. 3-3. If the input and feedback resistors are eliminated, the gain of an inverting amplifier will be 1.

Once again, the output's polarity is the opposite of the input's polarity.

The value of R3 is not terribly critical, but it should be approximately equal to the parallel combination of R1 and R2. That is:

$$R3 = (R1 \times R2)/(R1 + R2)$$

To illustrate this, let's return to our earlier example, in which R1 = 2.2 KΩ and R2 = 22 KΩ. In this case, the value of R3 should be about:

$$R3 = (2200 \times 22000)/(2200 + 22000) =$$
$$48,400,000/24,200 =$$
$$2000 \ \Omega$$

Since the exact value is not critical, we can use the nearest standard resistance value for R3. In this example, either a 1.8 KΩ or a 2.2 KΩ resistor may be used.

In some applications, the phase inversion produced by the circuit shown in Fig. 3-2 may be undesirable. To have the op-amp work as a non-inverting amplifier (buffer), the connections are made as shown in Fig. 3-4. In this circuit, the gain is defined as:

$$Av = 1 + R2/R1$$

The output is in phase (same polarity) with the input. Notice that the gain must always be at least 1 (unity). The non-inverting circuit can not be used for signal attenuation.

If R2 is considerably larger than R1, the gain will be relatively large. For example, if R1 = 10 KΩ and R2 = 470 KΩ, the circuit gain works out to:

$$Av = 1 + 470,000/10,000 =$$
$$1 + 47 =$$
$$48$$

If, on the other hand, R1 is considerably larger than R2, the gain will be just slightly greater than unity. For instance, if R1 = 100 KΩ and R2 = 22 KΩ the gain will be:

$$Av = 1 + 22,000/100,000 =$$
$$1 + 0.22 =$$
$$1.22$$

If the two resistances are equal (R1 = R2), the gain will always be 2. Try a few examples using the gain equation to prove this to yourself.

A special case is when both resistances are made equal to 0. That is, the resistors are replaced by direct connections, as shown in Fig. 3-5. Here, the gain is exactly unity. This is in keeping with the gain formula:

$$Av = 1 + R2/R1 =$$
$$1 + 0/0 =$$
$$1 + 0 =$$
$$1$$

The output is identical to the input. This non-inverting voltage follower circuit is used for buffer, isolation, and impedance matching applications.

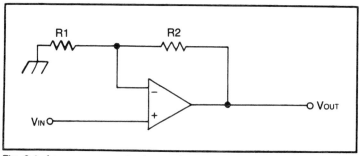

Fig. 3-4. An op-amp can also be used as a non-inverting amplifier.

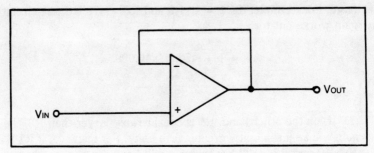

Fig. 3-5. A unity gain non-inverting amplifier can be used for buffer applications.

ADDER

An op-amp can be used to add multiple input voltages. Input signals V1, V2, ... Vn are applied to the op-amp through resistors R1, R2, ... Rn, as shown in Fig. 3-6. The output signal is then a combination of these signals, giving the sum of the inputs.

The actual performance of the op-amp as an adder can be calculated with this formula:

$$\text{VOUT} = -\text{Ro} \left((V1/R1) + (V2/R2) \ldots + (Vn/Rn) \right)$$

Note the minus sign. This indicates that the output is inverted (the polarity is reversed). That is, this circuit is an inverting adder.

By changing the connections to the inverting and non-inverting

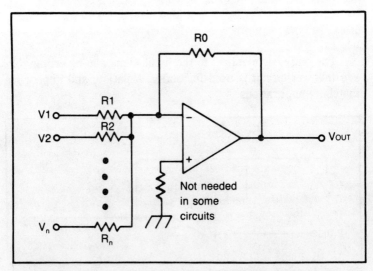

Fig. 3-6. Adder circuit based on an op-amp. This inverts the output.

24

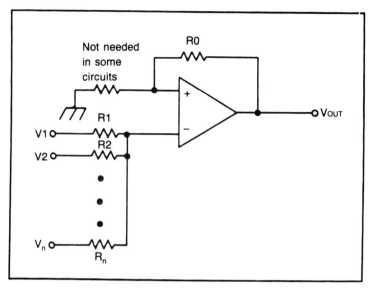

Fig. 3-7. Non-inverting adder circuit, i.e., the input and output have the same polarity of signal and are thus in phase.

inputs of the op-amp, as shown in Fig. 3-7, the circuit can be converted to a non-inverting adder.

If all of the input resistors have equal values, the output equation can be simplified to:

$$V_{OUT} = -R_O ((V1 + V2 \ldots + Vn)/R)$$

DIFFERENTIAL AMPLIFIER

A basic circuit for a differential amplifier is shown in Fig. 3-8. Component values are chosen so that R1 = R2 and R3 = R4. Performance is then given by:

$$V_{OUT} = V_{IN} 2 - V_{IN} 1$$

provided the op-amp used can accept the fact that the impedance for input 1 and input 2 is different (impedance for input 1 = R1; and impedance for input 2 = R1 + R3).

ADDER/SUBTRACTOR

Connections for an adder/subtractor circuit are shown in Fig. 3-9. If R1 and R2 are the same value; and R3 and R4 are also made

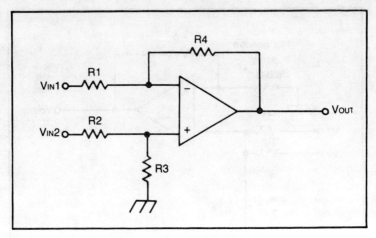

Fig. 3-8. Basic differential amplifier circuit.

the same value as each other, then:

$$V_{OUT} = V3 + V4 - V1 - V2$$

In other words, inputs to V3 and V4 give a summed output ($V_{OUT} = V3 + V4$). Inputs V1 and V2 subtract from the output voltage.

Values for R1, R2, and R3 and R4 are chosen to suit the op-amp characteristics. R5 should be the same value as R3 and R4; and R6 should be the same value as R1 and R2.

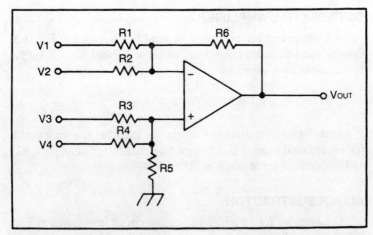

Fig. 3-9. Adder/subtractor circuit. See text for calculation of component values.

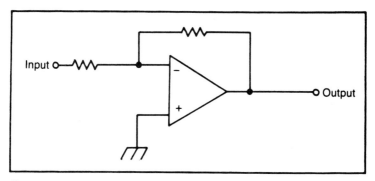

Fig. 3-10. This circuit is used to perform simple multiplication with a constant multiplier.

MULTIPLIER

The circuit shown in Fig. 3-10 can be used to perform simple multiplication. Note that this is the same circuit as Fig. 3-2. For accurate results, precision resistors of the specified values for R1 and R2 should be used to give a constant gain (and thus multiplication of input voltage in the ratio R2/R1). Note that this circuit inverts the phase of the output.

The output voltage will be equal to:

$$V_{OUT} = -(V_{IN} \times Av)$$

where V_{OUT} is the output voltage, V_{IN} is the input voltage, and Av is the gain as defined by R1 and R2.

If a variable resistance (potentiometer) is used for R2, as shown in Fig. 3-11, the multiplication constant can be varied. A calibration dial with markings for various typical gains should be placed

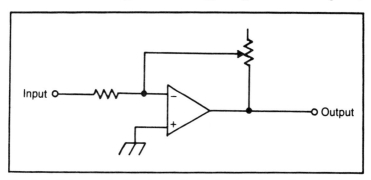

Fig. 3-11. Using a potentiometer as the feedback resistor allows the circuit to be used with a variable multiplier.

27

around the control shaft. This dial can be calibrated to read out the multiplication constant directly.

INTEGRATOR

Theoretically, at least, an op-amp will work as an *integrator* with the inverting input connected to the output via a capacitor. In practice, a resistor needs to be paralleled across this capacitor to provide *dc* stability as shown in Fig. 3-12.

This circuit integrates input signal with the following relationship applying:

$$V_{OUT} = \frac{1}{R1 \cdot C} \int V_{IN} \, dt$$

The value of R2 should be chosen to match the op-amp characteristics so that:

$$V_{OUT} = \frac{R2}{R1} \cdot V_{IN}$$

DIFFERENTIATOR

The differentiator circuit has a capacitor in the input line con-

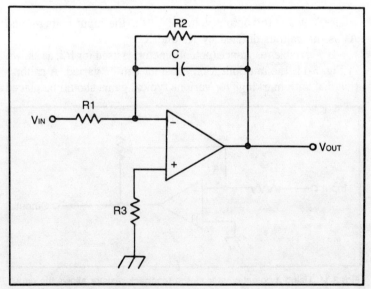

Fig. 3-12. Op-amp integrator circuit.

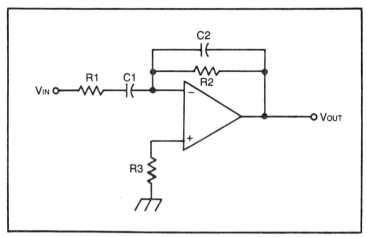

Fig. 3-13. Practical circuit for an op-amp differentiator.

necting to the inverting input, and a resistor connecting this input to output. Again this circuit has practical limitations, so a better configuration is to parallel the resistor with a capacitor as shown in Fig. 3-13.

The performance of this circuit is given by:

$$V_{OUT} = -R2\ C1\ \frac{dV_{IN}}{dt}$$

LOG AMPLIFIERS

The basic circuit (Fig. 3-14) uses an NPN transistor in conjunction with an op-amp to produce an output proportional to the log of the input:

$$V_{OUT} = -k\ log_{10}\ \frac{V_{IN}}{RI_o}$$

The lower diagram shows the "inverted" circuit, this time using a PNP transistor, to work as a basic *anti-log* amplifier.

The capacitor required is usually of small value (e.g., 20 pF).

LOG MULTIPLIERS

Logarithmic working of an op-amp is extended in Fig. 3-15 to give a *log multiplier.* Input X to one log amplifier gives *log X* output; and input Y to the second log amplifier gives *log Y* output.

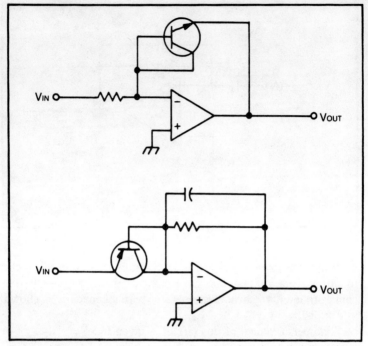

Fig. 3-14. Basic log amplifier circuits using a transistor in conjunction with an op-amp.

These are fed as inputs to a third op-amp to give an output *log XY*.

If this output is fed to an anti-log amplifier, the output is the inverted product of X and Y (i.e., *X. Y*).

LOG DIVIDER

The circuit shown in Fig. 3-16 is just the opposite of the one in Fig. 3-15. Here log and anti-log amp stages are used to perform division on the two input signals. The output is proportional to x/y.

AUDIO AMP

The op-amp is primarily a dc amplifier, but it can also be used for ac applications. Figure 3-17 shows a simple audio amplifier. More audio amplifier circuits will be presented in Chapter 4.

MIXER

This circuit (Fig. 3-18) is a variation on the audio amplifier. Note the similarity to the adder circuit shown in Fig. 3-6. The various

30

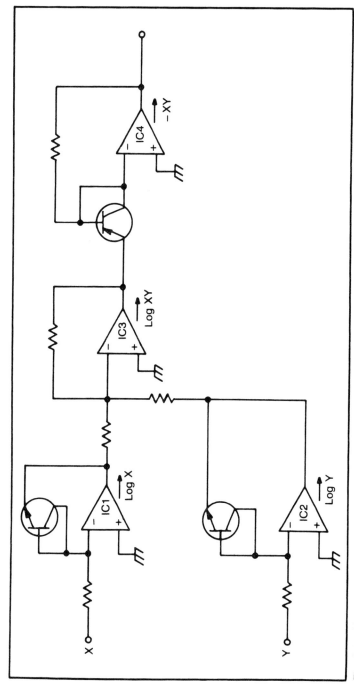

Fig. 3-15. Multiple log amplifier stages can be combined to perform true multiplication on two input signals.

31

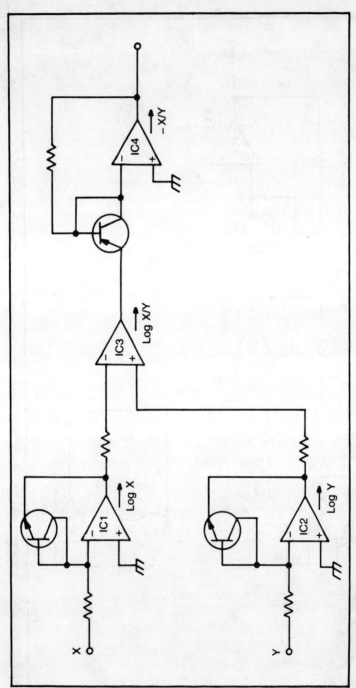

Fig. 3-16. Log amplifiers can also be used to perform division.

32

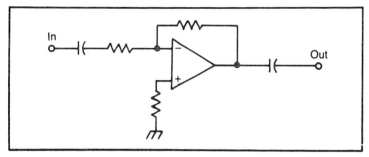

Fig. 3-17. Op-amps can be used for ac applications, as well as dc applications.

input signals are combined, or mixed. The level of each input signal can be adjusted via its input potentiometer. This allows the user to control the relative proportions of the various input signals in the output.

SIGNAL SPLITTER

The signal splitter circuit shown in Fig. 3-19 is just the reverse

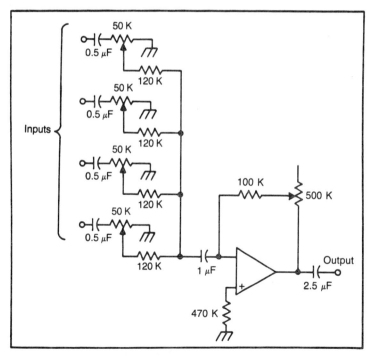

Fig. 3-18. This mixer circuit combines multiple audio inputs into a single output.

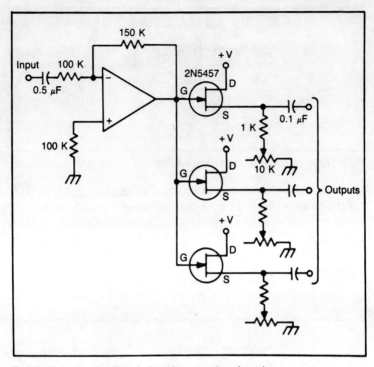

Fig. 3-19. A signal splitter is just the opposite of a mixer.

of a mixer. A single output signal is split off into multiple identical outputs to feed different inputs. This circuit is used to isolate the various signal paths from each other. Each output line has its own individual potentiometer to set the desired level.

VOLTAGE-TO-CURRENT CONVERTER

The circuit configuration shown in Fig. 3-20 will result in the same current flowing through R1 and the load impedance R2, the value of this current being independent of the load and proportional to the signal voltage, although it will be of relatively low value because of the high input resistance presented by the non-inverting terminal. The value of this current is directly proportional to $V_{IN}/R1$.

CURRENT-TO-VOLTAGE CONVERTER

This configuration (Fig. 3-21) enables the input signal current to flow directly through the feedback resistor R2 when the output

34

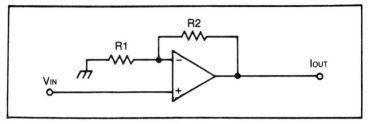

Fig. 3-20. Voltage-to-current converter using an op-amp.

voltage is equal to $I_{IN} \times R2$. In other words, input current is converted into a proportional output voltage. No current flows through R2, the lower limit of current flow being established by the bias circuit generated at the inverting input.

A capacitor may be added to this circuit, as shown in the diagram, to reduce "noise."

CURRENT SOURCE

Use of an op-amp as a current source is shown in Fig. 3-22. Resistor values are selected as follows:

$$R1 = R2$$
$$R3 = R4 + R5$$

Current output is given by:

$$I_{OUT} = \frac{R3 \bullet V_{IN}}{R1 \bullet R5}$$

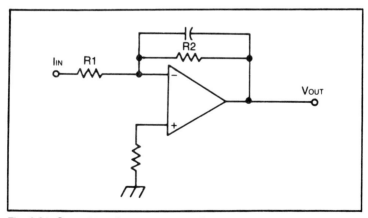

Fig. 3-21. Current-to-voltage converter using an op-amp.

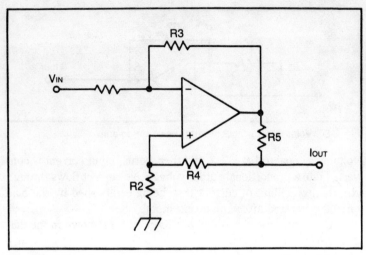

Fig. 3-22. Circuit for using an op-amp as a current source. See text for component values required.

MULTIVIBRATOR

An op-amp can be made to work as a multivibrator. Two basic circuits are shown in Fig. 3-23. The one on the top left is a free running (astable) multivibrator, the frequency of which is determined by:

$$f = \cfrac{1}{2C \bullet R1 \, \log_e \cfrac{2R3 + 1}{R2}}$$

The lower right hand diagram shows a monostable multivibrator circuit which can be triggered by a square wave pulse input. Component values given are for a CA741 op-amp. See also separate chapter on "Multivibrators."

SQUARE WAVE GENERATOR

A practical square wave generator circuit built around an op-amp is shown in Fig. 3-24. This is perhaps the simplest possible square wave generator circuit. Besides the op-amp itself, only three external resistors and a single capacitor are required.

Resistor R1 and capacitor C1 are the primary components in defining the time constant (output frequency) of the circuit. But the output frequency is also affected by the positive feedback net-

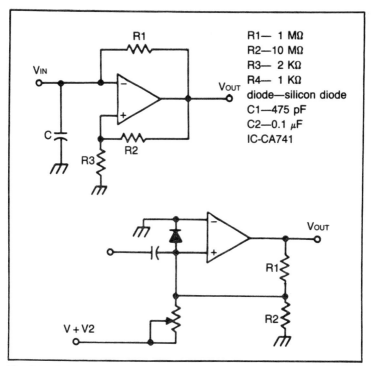

R1— 1 MΩ
R2—10 MΩ
R3— 2 KΩ
R4— 1 KΩ
diode—silicon diode
C1—475 pF
C2—0.1 μF
IC-CA741

Fig. 3-23. Two basic circuits for a multivibrator, based on op-amps.

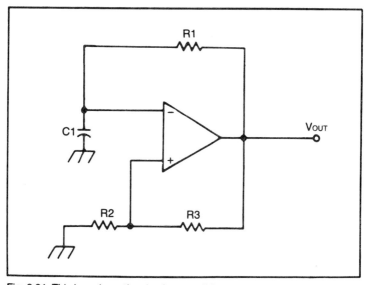

Fig. 3-24. This is perhaps the simplest possible square wave generator circuit.

37

work made up of R2 and R3. The general equations are rather complex, but they can be simplified for specific R3/R2 ratios. For instance:

$$\text{If } R3/R2 \approx 1.0 \text{ then } F \approx 0.5/(R1/C1)$$

or:

$$\text{If } R3/R2 \approx 10 \text{ then } F \approx 5/(R1/C1)$$

For most applications, the most practical approach is to use one of these standard ratios, and adjust the values of R1 and C1 to generate the desired frequency. Standardized values can be used for R2 and R3. For example, if R2 = 10K and R3 = 100K, the R3/R2 ratio will be 10, so:

$$F = 5/(R1/C1)$$

Generally, we will know the desired frequency and will need to select the appropriate component values. The easiest approach is to first select a likely value for C1, and then rearrange the equation to solve for the value of R1:

$$R1 = 5/(FC1)$$

Let's try a typical example. We want to generate a 1200 Hz square wave signal. If we use a 0.22 μF capacitor for C1, the value of R1 should be:

$$R1 = 5/(1200 \times 0.00000022) = 5/0.000264 = 18{,}940 \ \Omega$$

For most applications, a standard 18K resistor could be used.

This circuit can be made even more useful and versatile by adding a potentiometer in series with R1, as shown in Fig. 3-25. This allows the output frequency to be manually changed.

The same equations are used for this circuit, except the value of R1 is equal to the series combination of fixed resistor R1a, and the adjusted value of potentiometer R1b;

$$R1 = R1a + R1b$$

The fixed resistor is included to prevent the value of R1 from ever becoming zero. The fixed value of R1a and the maximum re-

38

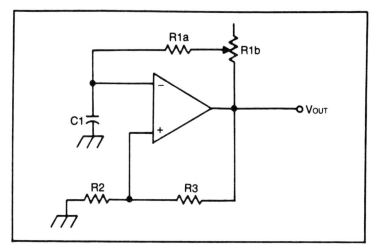

Fig. 3-25. The basic square wave generator can be adapted easily for variable frequency output.

sistance of R1b sets the range of output frequencies.

VARIABLE PULSE WIDTH GENERATOR

A square wave is perfectly symmetrical. That is, it is in its high state for exactly one half of each cycle, as illustrated in Fig. 3-26. The ratio of the high level time to the total cycle time is called the duty cycle of the signal. The duty cycle of a square wave is, by definition, 1:2.

Closely related to square waves are rectangle waves and pulse waves. These waveforms also switch between a high and a low state, but have different duty cycles. The terms "rectangle wave" and "pulse wave" are used somewhat interchangeably, although usually, a pulse wave is considered to have a relatively short high level time.

Figure 3-27 shows a rectangle wave with a duty cycle of 1:3. The output level is high for one third of each cycle. The rectangle wave illustrated in Fig. 3-28 has a duty cycle of 1:4.

We can convert the square-wave generator described in the preceding section into a rectangle wave generator by adding just two components. The revised circuit is shown in Fig. 3-29.

On negative half-cycles, diode D1 blocks flow of current through R4. The time constant is comprised of R1 and C1:

$$T1 = 5/(2C1 \cdot R1)$$

39

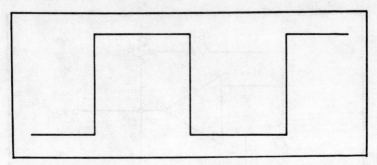

Fig. 3-26. A square wave is symmetrical. It is high for one half of each complete cycle.

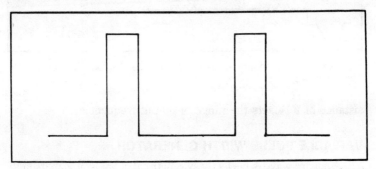

Fig. 3-27. A rectangle wave with a 1:3 duty cycle is high for one third of each complete cycle.

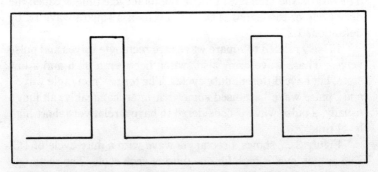

Fig. 3-28. A rectangle wave with a 1:4 duty cycle is high for one fourth of each complete cycle.

On positive half-cycles, however, the diode conducts and the time constant is defined by C1 and the parallel combination of R1 and R4:

$$T2 = 5/(201 \bullet ((R1 \bullet R4)/(R1 + R4)))$$

The length of the total cycle is simply the sum of the two half-cycle time constants:

$$Tt = T1 + T2$$

The output frequency is the reciprocal of the total time constant of the complete cycle:

$$F = 1/Tt$$

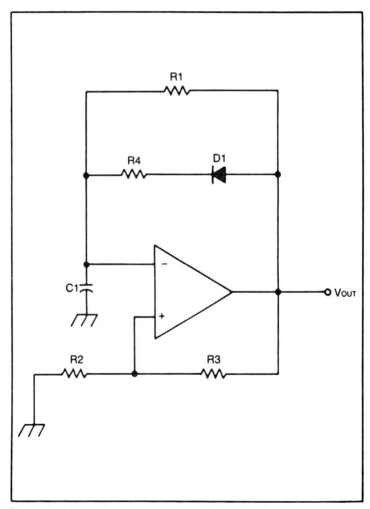

Fig. 3-29. This circuit generates asymmetrical rectangle waves.

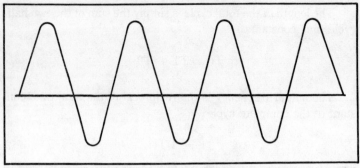

Fig. 3-30. The sine wave is the simplest ac signal.

Since the time constant will be different for the high and low level portions of the cycle, the duty cycle will be something other than 1:2. The output waveform becomes asymmetrical.

Either R1 or R4, or both, may be made variable, but bear in mind that changing either of these resistances affects both the output frequency and the duty cycle.

SINE WAVE OSCILLATOR

The simplest of all ac signals is the sine wave, which is illustrated in Fig. 3-30. This is a very pure signal with no harmonic content at all. A sine wave consists of only a single fundamental frequency.

Actually, it is quite difficult to generate a truly pure, distortion free, sine wave. Fortunately, we can come close to the ideal with an oscillator circuit built around an op-amp.

A typical sine wave oscillator circuit using an op-amp is shown in Fig. 3-31. The feedback network is a twin-T circuit, which functions as a band-reject (or notch) Filter. Resistors R1 and R2 along with capacitor C1 form one T. The other T is made up of C2, C3, R3, and R4. It is upside down in the schematic.

For this circuit to function properly, the component values must have the following relationships:

$$R2 = R1$$
$$R3 = R1/4$$
$$R4 = R1/2 \text{ (approximate)}$$
$$C1 = 2C2$$
$$C3 = C2$$

The output frequency is determined by this formula:

$$F = 1/(6.28 \bullet R1 \bullet C2)$$

The twin-T feedback network is detuned slightly by adjusting the value of R4. This will usually be a miniature trimmer potentiometer. The potentiometer is set for its maximum resistance, then slowly decreased, until the circuit just begins to break into oscillation. If the resistance is set low, the sine wave will be distorted at the output.

SCHMITT TRIGGER

A *Schmitt trigger* is known technically as a *regenerative compa-*

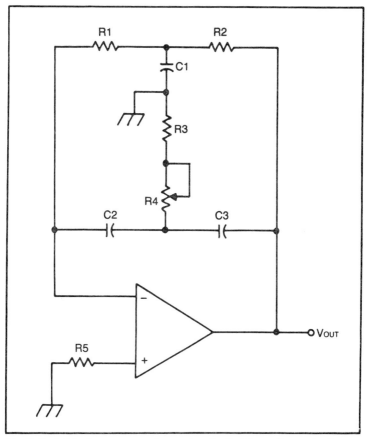

Fig. 3-31. A fair sine wave can be produced with this oscillator circuit.

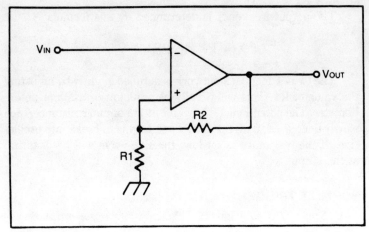

Fig. 3-32. Schmitt trigger which gives an output once a precise value of varying input voltage is reached. An application of this circuit is a *dc* voltage level senser.

parator. Its main use is to convert a slowly varying input voltage into an output signal at a precise value of input voltage. In other words it acts as a voltage "trigger" with a "backlash" feature, called hysteresis.

The op-amp is a simple basis for a Schmitt trigger (see Fig. 3-32). The triggering or *trip* voltage is determined by:

$$V \text{ trip} = \frac{V_{OUT} \cdot R1}{-R1 + R2}$$

The hysteresis of such a circuit is twice the trip voltage.

Another Schmitt trigger circuit is shown in Fig. 3-33, the triggering point being approximately one-fifth of the supply voltage, i.e., there is a "triggered" output once the *dc* input reaches one-fifth the value of the supply voltage. The supply voltage can range from 6 to 15 volts, thus the trigger can be made to work at anything from 1.2 to 3 volts, depending on the supply voltage used. The actual triggering point can also be adjusted by using different values for R4, if required.

Once triggered, the output will be equal to that of the supply voltage. If output is connected to a filament bulb or LED (with ballast resistor in series), the bulb (or LED) will light once the input voltage has risen to the triggering voltage and thus indicate that this specific voltage level has been reached at the input.

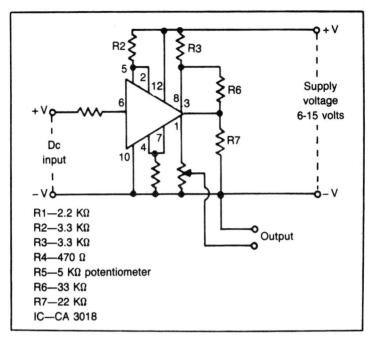

Fig. 3-33. A more complicated Schmitt trigger circuit for general use.

R1—2.2 KΩ
R2—3.3 KΩ
R3—3.3 KΩ
R4—470 Ω
R5—5 KΩ potentiometer
R6—33 KΩ
R7—22 KΩ
IC—CA 3018

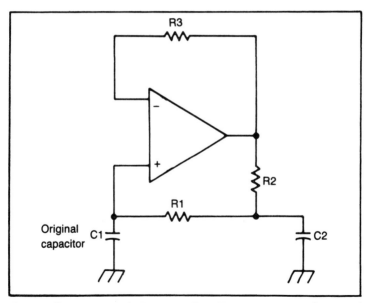

Fig. 3-34. Capacitance multiplier circuit. The effective capacitance Ce is equal to the value of C1 multiplied by R1/R2.

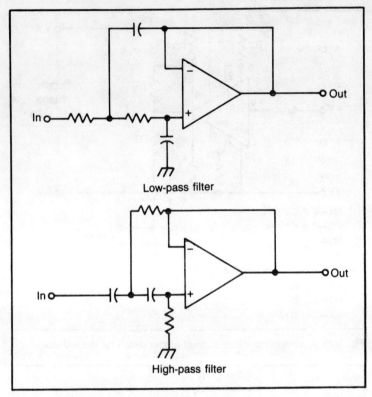

Fig. 3-35. Two basic filter circuits using op-amps.

CAPACITANCE BOOSTER

The circuit shown in Fig. 3-34 works as a *multiplier* for the capacitor C1, i.e., associated with a fixed value of C1 it gives an effective capacitance Ce which can be many times greater. The actual multiplication ratio is R1/R2 so that making R1 ten times greater than R2, say, means that the effective capacitance of this circuit would be 10 × C1.

As far as utilization of such a multiplier is concerned, the circuit now also contains resistance (R2) in series with the effective capacitance.

FILTERS

Op-amps are widely used as basic components in filter circuits. Two basic circuits are shown in Fig. 3-35. (See also separate chapter on Filters.)

46

Chapter 4

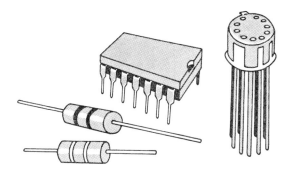

Audio Amplifiers

Quite a number of linear ICs are designed as audio amplifiers for use in radio receivers, record players, etc. Again these are used with external components, but physical layout and the length of leads is relatively unimportant—unlike circuits carrying radio frequencies. The "packaging" of such ICs can vary from cans (usually TO-5 to TO-100 configuration) to dual-in-line and quad-in-line. In all cases they will usually have 12 or 14 leads (but sometimes less). Not all these leads are necessarily used in a working circuit. They are there to provide access to different parts of the integrated circuit for different applications. Integrated circuits designed with higher power ratings may also incorporate a tab or tabs to be connected to a heat sink; or a copper slug on top of the package for a similar purpose.

A single chip can contain one, two, three or more amplifier stages interconnected and following each other (technically referred to as being in *cascade*). Pin-out connections provide "tapping" points for using one or more stages separately or in cascade as required.

The (RCA) CA3035 integrated circuit is just one example. It consists of three separate amplifier stages connected in cascade with a component count equivalent to 10 transistors, 1 diode and 15 resistors. Each amplifier stage has different characteristics. The first stage, which can be selected by connections to pins 1, 2, 3, 9 and 10 (see Fig. 4-1), is a wide band amplifier characterized by high input resistance (i.e., ideally suited to connecting to a preced-

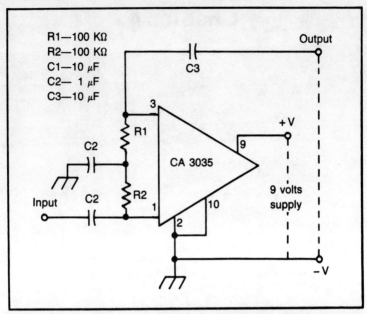

R1—100 KΩ
R2—100 KΩ
C1—10 μF
C2— 1 μF
C3—10 μF

Fig. 4-1. Utilization of the first amplifier in CA3035 integrated circuit by tapping pins 1, 2, 3, 9 and 10. This circuit gives a voltage gain of 100-160 with an input resistance of 50 KΩ and an output resistance of 270 Ω.

ing transistor stage). The working circuit using this stage in Fig. 4-1. It has a gain of the order of 160 (44 dB).

The second amplifier in the CA3035 has a lower input resistance (2 KΩ) and a low output resistance of 170 Ω. The gain is similar to the first stage (about 45 dB). A working circuit with tapping points is shown in Fig. 4-2.

The third amplifier is a wide band amplifier with a low input resistance (670 Ω) and a high output resistance (5 KΩ). It offers a voltage gain of 100 (40 dB). A working circuit is shown in Fig. 4-3.

Amplifiers 1 and 2 can be cascaded; or amplifiers 2 and 3; or amplifiers 1, 2 and 3. Figure 4-4 shows the external connections and components required to cascade amplifiers 1 and 2.

Using all three amplifiers in cascade results in a gain of approximately 110 dB. The circuit in this case is shown in Fig. 4-5.

MODIFYING AMPLIFIER PERFORMANCE

The output impedance of an amplifier stage can be modified by connecting R1 to provide a negative feedback from output to input. This has the effect of reducing the working value of R1 and

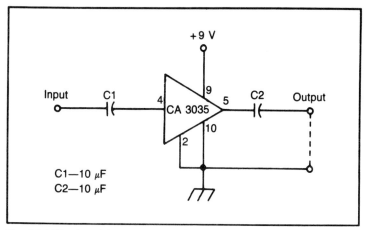

Fig. 4-2. Utilization of the second amplifier in CA3035 integrated circuit by tapping pins 2, 4, 5, 9 and 10. This circuit gives a voltage gain of 100-120 with an input resistance of 2 Ω and an output resistance of 170 Ω.

R1/Av where Av is the amplifier open loop voltage gain. This is accomplished without affecting the actual voltage gain. In the case of cascaded amplifiers a capacitor C2 is needed in series with R1 to act as a block to dc (i.e., R1 only is needed for amplifier 1 part

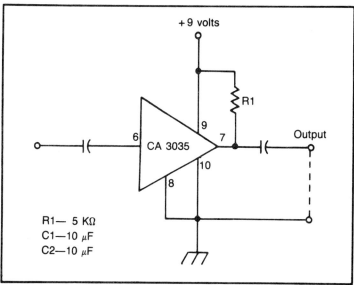

Fig. 4-3. Utilization of the third amplifier in CA3035 integrated circuit by tapping pins 6, 7, 8, 9 and 10. This circuit gives a voltage gain of 80-120 with an input resistance of 670 Ω and an output resistance of 5 KΩ.

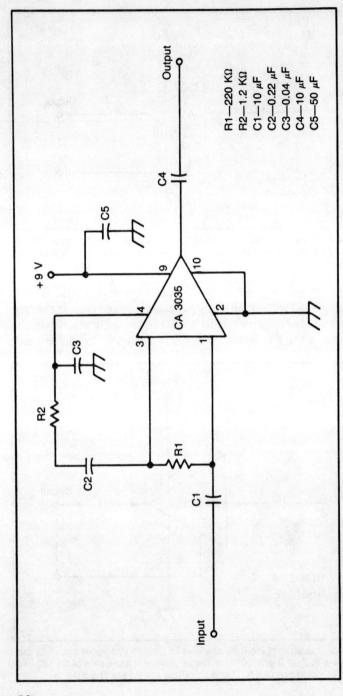

R1—220 KΩ
R2—1.2 KΩ
C1—10 μF
C2—0.22 μF
C3—0.04 μF
C4—10 μF
C5—50 μF

Fig. 4-4. Circuit for using first and second amplifiers contained in CA3035 in cascade. This circuit gives a voltage gain of about 7000 with an input of 50 Ω and an output resistance of 170 Ω.

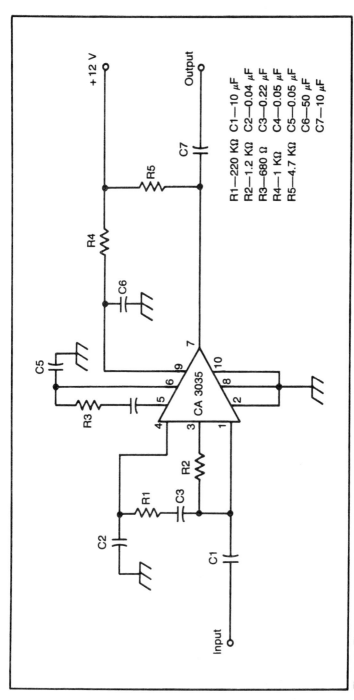

Fig. 4-5. This circuit shows all three amplifiers in CA3035 cascaded to give a voltage gain of about 200,000.

R1—220 KΩ   C1—10 µF
R2—1.2 KΩ   C2—0.04 µF
R3—680 Ω   C3—0.22 µF
R4—1 KΩ   C4—0.05 µF
R5—4.7 KΩ   C5—0.05 µF
            C6—50 µF
            C7—10 µF

of CA 3035, C1 being effective as a blocking capacitor in this case). Since amplifier 2 in this chip is directly coupled to amplifier 1 and amplifier 2 is directly coupled to amplifier 3 the use of an impedance-matching resistor applied to amplifier 2 (or amplifier 3) will require the use of a blocking capacitor in series with the resistor.

The gain of the amplifier stage can be modified by the use of a series resistor in the input (R1). This acts as a potential divider in conjunction with the effective input resistance of the stage so that only a proportion of the input signal is applied to the stage. In this case:

- actual voltage gain = $\dfrac{R1}{Ri + R1/Av}$

- input resistance = $Ri + R1/Av$

where Ri is the input resistance of the IC

Thus by suitable choice of R1 and Ri, both voltage gain and input resistance of an amplifier circuit can be modified to match specific requirements. It follows that if a number of different resistors are used for Ri, the circuit can be given different response (sensitivity) for a given input applied to each value of Ri by switching. This mode of working is useful for preamplifiers. Virtually the same circuit is used for an audio mixer, separate input channels being connected by separate series resistors (Ri) and thence commonly connected to the input. In this case each channel has the same input resistance with an overall gain of unity.

Figure 4-6 shows a circuit for a low power (1.8 watt) audio amplifier using a TA 611 monolithic integrated circuit. This particular IC is available in two configurations, a TO-100 metal case and in a quad-in-line plastic package. Lead positions are shown in Fig. 4-7 for the two different configurations.

This is a particularly attractive circuit for it needs a minimum number of external components and is capable of driving an 8-ohm loudspeaker directly with any supply voltage between 6 volts and 12 volts. Also, it does not require a heat sink.

Exactly the same circuit can be used with a number of other integrated circuits in the same family, offering higher output powers. These are the TA611B and TA611C. The only difference is the values required for the external components required. (See Table 4-1 for a comparison.)

Lead arrangement for the TA611B and TA611C are the same

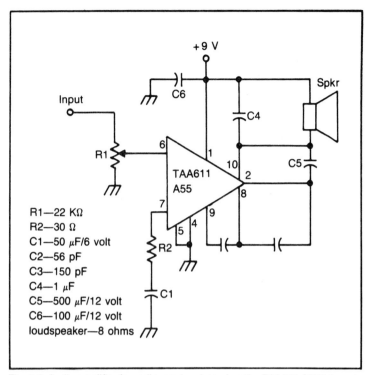

+9 V

Spkr

Input

C6

C4

R1

6

1

10

C5

TAA611
A55

2

7

8

9

5

4

R2

C1

R1—22 KΩ
R2—30 Ω
C1—50 μF/6 volt
C2—56 pF
C3—150 pF
C4—1 μF
C5—500 μF/12 volt
C6—100 μF/12 volt
loudspeaker—8 ohms

Fig. 4-6. Audio amplifier for radio receiver based on the TAA611 A55 integrated circuit. Pin numbers shown are for the can-shaped version of this IC.

as TAA611A12.

Because of its higher power, the circuit based on the TA611C really requires the IC to be mounted with a heat sink although this is not absolutely essential. The IC is, in fact, available with a special mounting bar or spacer to which a heat sink can be attached. The recommended method of mounting is shown in Fig. 4-8, the heat sink itself being a piece of aluminum sheet cut to a suitable size and bent to the shape shown. The IC itself has a copper slug on its top face on to which the heat sink sits (and is clamped down by the mounting bolts). Better thermal contact between the IC and the heat sink can be achieved if the contact area is very lightly coated with silicon grease.

There are other methods of fitting heat sinks to this IC (and other types). The TA611C is also available with an external bar, the ends of which can be soldered to copper "patches" on the printed circuit panel (also shown in Fig. 4-8). In this example the

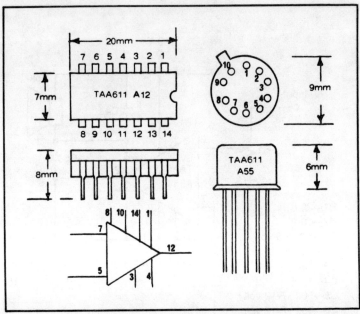

Fig. 4-7. The two versions of the TAA611 integrated circuit. The TAA611 A55 is a 14-pin dual-in-line package. The TAA611 A55 is a "can" shape package in a metal case (TO-100). The circuits are identical so either can be used in Fig. 4-1 with the same external components. Note, however, the different pin-out arrangement for the TAA611 A12 on the left.

copper areas form the actual heat sink. A suitable area in this case would be about 30 mm square for each copper patch. These copper areas are, of course, merely used for heat dissipation and are not part of the actual printed circuit as such, although it is normally advisable—and necessary with some types of IC—to connect the

Table 4-1. Comparison of TA611B and TA611C.

	TA611B	TA611C
Supply Voltage	6-15	6-18
Max. Power Output	2.1 watts	3.3 watts
R1	22 KΩ	220 KΩ
R2	30 Ω	150 Ω
C1	50 μF	25 μF
C2	56 pF	82 pF
C3	150 pF	1.2 μF
C4	omit	omit
C5	500 μF	500 μF
C6	100 μF	100 μF

54

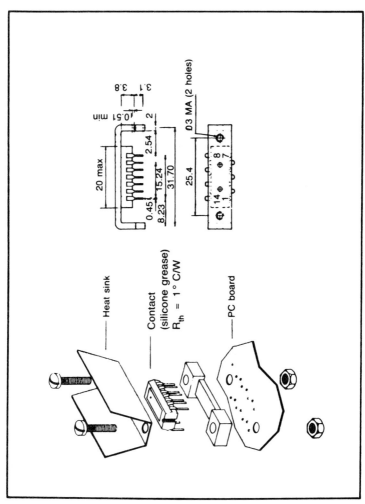

Fig. 4-8. Aluminum sheet heat sink applied to the TA611C integrated circuit (left) and alternative external bar fitted to this IC (right) for connecting to heat sink areas on copper of printed circuit board.

heat sink area to the common earth of the circuit. It is just a convenient method of making heat sinks integral with the printed circuit panel.

A further audio amplifier based on a TBA641B integrated circuit is shown in Fig. 4-9. This is a little more complicated in terms of the number of external components used, but has the advantage of driving a 4-Ω speaker (the more readily available value with larger loudspeakers) and is suitable for direct coupling of the input. It will operate on a supply voltage ranging from 6 volts to 16 volts and give 4.5 watts output power at 14 volts. Again the IC needs mounting with a heat sink of the type illustrated in Fig. 4-8.

SHORT CIRCUIT PROTECTION

A feature of many audio amplifier circuits is that if the output is shorted when the circuit is switched on (e.g., loudspeaker con-

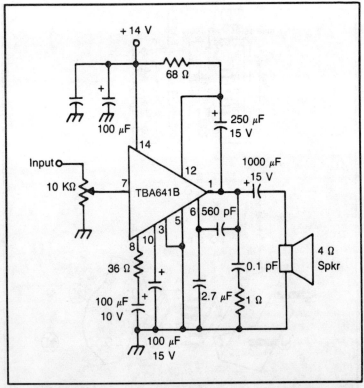

Fig. 4-9. Audio amplifier for 4 Ω loudspeaker based on the TBA641B integrated circuit. Component values are shown on the diagram (SGS-Gates).

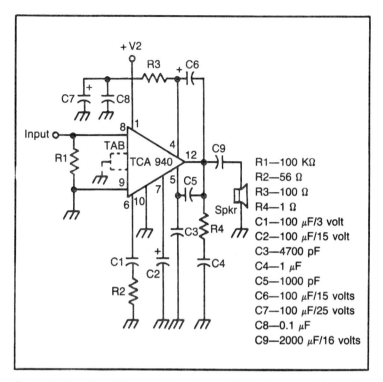

Fig. 4-10. 10-watt amplifier circuit based on the TCA940 integrated circuit. The TCA940 is a 12-lead quad-in-line plastic package.

nections accidentally shorted), excessive current may be passed by the output transistors sufficient to destroy them. It is possible to provide short-circuit protection with additional circuitry limiting the current which can flow through the output transistors. This can readily be incorporated in an IC, an example being the TCA940 designed as a 10 watt class B amplifier. Other characteristics of this particular IC are high output current (up to 3 amps) very low harmonic and crossover distortion and a thermal shut down feature (See later).

The circuit is shown in Fig. 4-10. Supply voltage is up to 24 volts. Power rating depends both on the supply voltage used and the resistance of the loudspeaker:

Supply voltage	4-Ω speaker	8-Ω speaker
20	10 watts	6.5 watts
18	9 watts	5 watts
16	7 watts	

A feature of this circuit is that the bandwidth is controlled by the values of R2 and C3 and C7. For a value of R2 = 56 Ω with C3 = 1000 pF and C7 = 5000 pF the bandwidth is 20 kHz. For the same capacitor values the bandwidth can be reduced to 10 kHz by making R2 = 20 Ω. For the original resistor value (R2 = 56 Ω), the bandwidth can be reduced to 10 kHz by making C3 = 2000 pF and C7 = 10000 pF.

Circuit assembly is straightforward, except that the IC needs a heat sink. It is provided with tabs which should be bolted to an external aluminum sheet heat sink of generous area.

THERMAL SHUT DOWN

The short-circuit protection built into this IC effectively works as a power-limiting device. It is only effective on a short-duration basis, i.e., to provide protection against temporary overload and short circuiting of the output. An additional circuit is included to ensure that regardless of how long a short circuit is present across the output the junction temperature of the output transistors is kept within safe limits.

In other words, this additional piece of circuitry incorporated in the IC provides complete protection against a shorted output. It also has another advantage. The same protection is present if there is another cause of overheating, e.g., the heat sink used is not really large enough for the job it is intended to do. The thermal shut-down circuitry simply reacts to the junction temperature becoming too high by reducing the output current and power to compensate.

HI-FI STEREO AMPLIFIER

The excellent performance and extremely good stability possible with integrated circuits makes them a logical choice for Hi-Fi circuits. The TDA 2020 monolithic integrated operational amplifier is an excellent up-to-date example of such a device, designed to be used as a Class B audio power amplifier for Hi-Fi circuits. It is capable of providing a 20-watt power output into a 4-Ω loudspeaker with a supply voltage of 18 volts, and with a guaranteed output power of 15 watts. It is also a device for providing high output current (up to 3.5 amps) and has a very low harmonic and crossover distortion. It also incorporates short-circuit protection and thermal shut-down protection.

The TDA2020 is in the form of a quad-in-line plastic package of conventional appearance with 14 leads. Because of its high power rating, it is intended to be used with a specially formed heat sink mounted on a spacer designed to provide proper thermal contact between the IC itself and the heat sink when assembled on two bolts—Fig. 4-11. The most negative supply voltage of the circuit is connected to the copper slug on the IC and hence also to the heat sink.

The basic amplifier circuit is completed by the addition of four external resistors and seven capacitors, plus a coupling capacitor to enable the circuit to be used with a split power supply. This provides direct drive for a 4-Ω loudspeaker. Since the Hi-Fi circuits are usually stereo, two ICs are used in this basic circuit configuration, each IC powering its own loudspeaker. The complete circuit is shown in Fig. 4-12.

A simpler stereo audio amplifier circuit is shown in Fig. 4-13, based on the (Mullard) TDA1009 integrated circuit. This IC is a low frequency Class B amplifier with no crossover distortion designed for use with a minimum number of external components. It delivers 2 × 6 watts output power at 10 percent distortion into speakers of 4-Ω impedance with 8 to 16 volts supply; and can also deliver the same power into speakers with 8-Ω impedance using a 24-volt supply. The IC incorporates short circuit protection for supply voltages up to 16 volts and also thermal protection. Input impedance is 45 KΩ.

The addition of capacitors C9 and C10 (shown dotted) provides "bootstrapping." This provides increased output power.

STEREO PREAMP

In many systems, a preamplifier stage is required to bring the input signal up to a sufficient level for proper operation for the main power amplifier. A turntable with a magnetic cartridge produces a very low level signal. A preamplifier is normally required.

In many stereo systems, the preamplifier stage also includes the volume and tone controls, and switching for selecting between the various input sources (turntable, FM receiver, tape deck, etc.).

A typical stereo preamp circuit is shown in Fig. 4-14. For simplicity, only the right channel is shown here. The left channel is identical. The 381A contains two independent preamplifier circuits, so a stereo (two channel) preamplifier can be constructed around a single IC. The pin numbers in parentheses are for the left channel. Pins 4 and 9 are the power supply connections, and are common to both halves of the circuit.

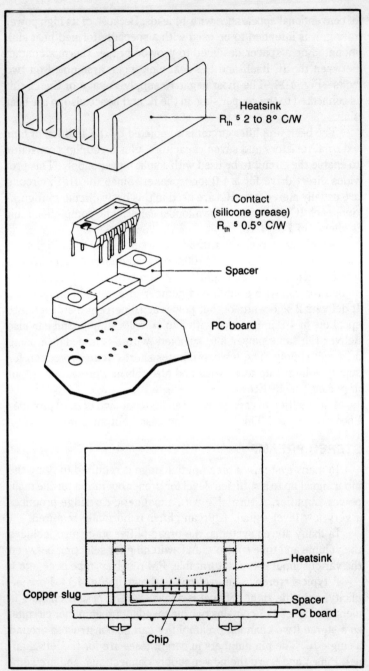

Heatsink
R_{th} ⁵ 2 to 8° C/W

Contact
(silicone grease)
R_{th} ⁵ 0.5° C/W

Spacer

PC board

Heatsink

Copper slug

Spacer

PC board

Chip

Fig. 4-11. Heat sink for the TDA2020 integrated circuit.

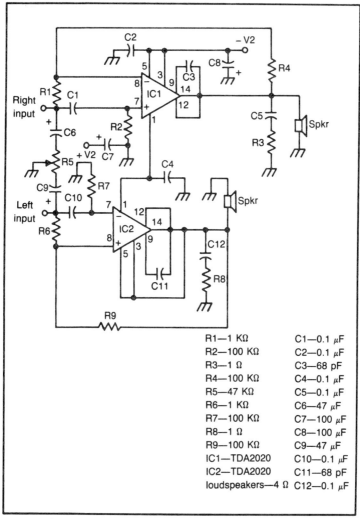

R1—1 KΩ	C1—0.1 µF
R2—100 KΩ	C2—0.1 µF
R3—1 Ω	C3—68 pF
R4—100 KΩ	C4—0.1 µF
R5—47 KΩ	C5—0.1 µF
R6—1 KΩ	C6—47 µF
R7—100 KΩ	C7—100 µF
R8—1 Ω	C8—100 µF
R9—100 KΩ	C9—47 µF
IC1—TDA2020	C10—0.1 µF
IC2—TDA2020	C11—68 pF
loudspeakers—4 Ω	C12—0.1 µF

Fig. 4-12. Stereo amplifier circuit with split supply voltage ± 17 to ± 24 volts.

This circuit features independent volume controls and source selection switching, but no tone controls. If you'd like to adapt the circuit to include tone controls, just bear in mind that a tone control is nothing more than a variable filter. Chapter 10 should give you plenty of information for designing tone controls.

Logarithmic taper potentiometers should be used for the volume controls.

Another stereo preamplifier for magnetic phono cartridge in-

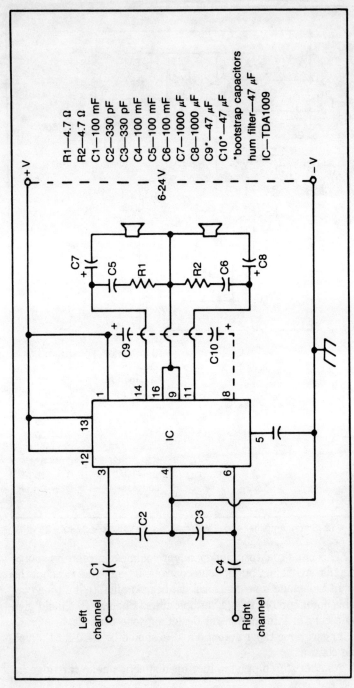

Fig. 4-13. Simple 2 × 6 watt stereo amplifier.

R1—4.7 Ω
R2—4.7 Ω
C1—100 mF
C2—330 pF
C3—330 pF
C4—100 mF
C5—100 mF
C6—100 mF
C7—1000 µF
C8—1000 µF
C9*—47 µF
C10*—47 µF
*bootstrap capacitors
hum filter—47 µF
IC—TDA1009

6-24 V

62

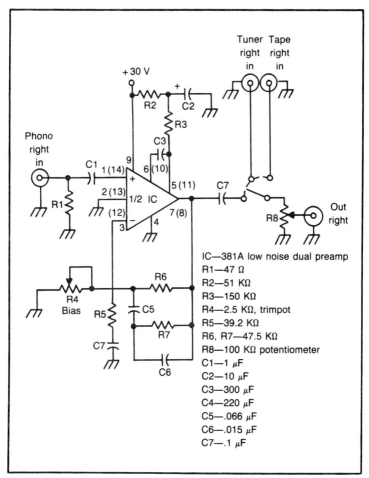

Tuner right in

Tape right in

Phono right in

+30 V

R2

C2

R3

C3

C1 1(14)

9

6(10)

5(11)

C7

Out right

R8

2(13)

1/2 IC

(12)

7(8)

R1

3

4

R4 Bias

R6

R5

C5

C7

R7

C6

IC—381A low noise dual preamp
R1—47 Ω
R2—51 KΩ
R3—150 KΩ
R4—2.5 KΩ, trimpot
R5—39.2 KΩ
R6, R7—47.5 KΩ
R8—100 KΩ potentiometer
C1—1 μF
C2—10 μF
C3—300 μF
C4—220 μF
C5—.066 μF
C6—.015 μF
C7—.1 μF

Fig. 4-14. Stereo preamp.

put is shown in Fig. 4-15. Both channels are shown.

This circuit is built around two sections of a 381 low noise dual preamplifier IC. In addition to independent volume controls, this circuit features independent bass and treble (tone) controls for each channel, and a balance control to set the relative levels of the two channels.

HIGH POWER AMPLIFIERS

Most of the original IC audio amplifiers which appeared on the market had a relatively limited power output and thus needed to be associated with a further stage or stages of transistor amplifi-

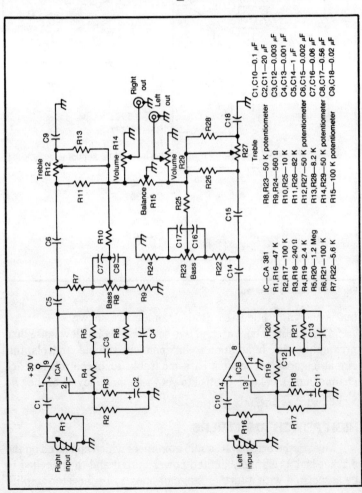

Fig. 4-15. Magnetic cartridge preamp.

C1,C10—0.1 μF
C2,C11—20 μF
C3,C12—0.003 μF
C4,C13—0.001 μF
C5,C14—1 μF
C6,C15—0.002 μF
C7,C16—0.06 μF
C8,C17—0.56 μF
C9,C18—0.02 μF

R8,R23—50 K potentiometer
R9,R24—560 Ω
R10,R25—10 K
R11,R26—82 K
R12,R27—50 K potentiometer
R13,R28—8.2 K
R14,R29—50 K potentiometer
R15—100 K potentiometer

IC—CA 381
R1,R16—47 K
R2,R17—100 K
R3,R18—240 Ω
R4,R19—2.4 K
R5,R20—1.2 Meg
R6,R21—100 K
R7,R22—5.6 K

cation to give more than a few watts output. Single IC amplifier chips are now readily available with output powers from 1 to 5 watts and substantially higher outputs are obtainable from later developments capable of handling even higher voltages and currents with satisfactory thermal stability.

BRIDGE AMPLIFIERS

Even higher outputs are obtainable from *bridge amplifier* circuits. These can be used to increase power from output for a given supply voltage, or maintain a high power output with a reduced supply voltage. Bridge connection can give four times the output power under a given load with the same supply voltage; or twice the output power at a fixed peak current if the load impedance is doubled (e.g., using 8-Ω loudspeaker(s) instead of 4-Ω loudspeaker(s)).

An example of this type of circuitry, again using the TDA2020 integrated circuit is shown in Fig. 4-16. It is capable of delivering 30 watts power output in an 8-Ω loudspeaker with a supply voltage of ± 17 volts.

RIAA AMPLIFIER

Theoretically, an amplifier's frequency response should be absolutely flat. That is, all frequencies should be amplified by exactly the same amount.

In some recording and transmission media, it may be necessary to pre-emphasize certain frequency components that could be attenuated excessively by the recording/transmission process. During playback/reception these same frequency components need to be de-emphasized to restore flat response.

Standard pre-emphasis/de-emphasis curves have been devised for various media to ensure interchangeability between sources. Virtually all phonograph records, for example, are recorded with the RIAA standard curve. An amplifier in a record player should include an RIAA de-emphasis network. A typical circuit for a ceramic cartridge input is shown in Fig. 4-17.

TAPE PLAYER AMPLIFIER

The circuit shown in Fig. 4-18 is designed as a playback amplifier for a tape deck. The standard NAB equalization curve is matched by the feedback network.

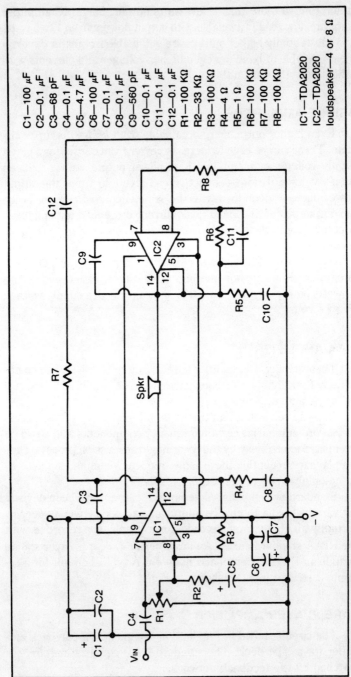

C1—100 µF
C2—0.1 µF
C3—68 pF
C4—0.1 µF
C5—4.7 µF
C6—100 µF
C7—0.1 µF
C8—0.1 µF
C9—560 pF
C10—0.1 µF
C11—0.1 µF
C12—0.1 µF
R1—100 KΩ
R2—33 KΩ
R3—100 KΩ
R4—4 Ω
R5—1 Ω
R6—100 KΩ
R7—100 KΩ
R8—100 KΩ

IC1—TDA2020
IC2—TDA2020
loudspeaker—4 or 8 Ω

Fig. 4-16. Powerful Bridge Amplifier.

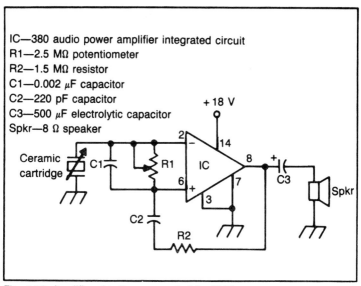

Fig. 4-17. Amplifier circuit compensated for RIAA.

In the figure:

IC—380 audio power amplifier integrated circuit
R1—2.5 MΩ potentiometer
R2—1.5 MΩ resistor
C1—0.002 μF capacitor
C2—220 pF capacitor
C3—500 μF electrolytic capacitor
Spkr—8 Ω speaker

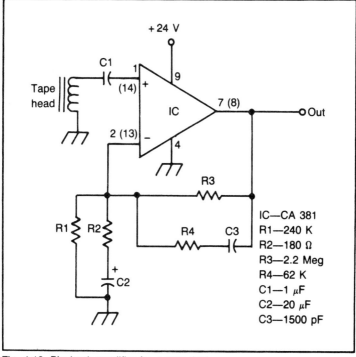

Fig. 4-18. Playback amplifier for a tape deck.

In the figure:

IC—CA 381
R1—240 K
R2—180 Ω
R3—2.2 Meg
R4—62 K
C1—1 μF
C2—20 μF
C3—1500 pF

The tape head should be selected to generate about 800 μV at 1 kHz. The output is approximately 5 volts RMS. An external volume control potentiometer can be added to the output line.

Chapter 5

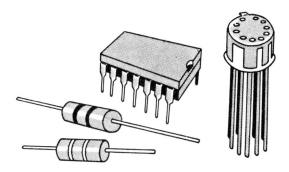

Complete Radio Circuits

The development of radio circuits around a single IC with the same physical size (and shape) as a single transistor is exemplified by the following. The IC is the Ferranti ZN414 which contains the equivalent of 10 transistors in a complete trf (tuned radio frequency) circuit providing three stages of rf application, a detector and *agc* (automatic gain control).

The ZN414 has three leads, identified as input, output and ground. It provides a complete radio circuit in itself to be connected to an external tuned circuit, an output decoupling capacitor, a feedback resistor and second decoupling capacitor, and an agc resistor. As with any high gain rf device, certain requirements should be observed to ensure stable and reliable operation. These are:

- All leads connecting components to the ICs should be kept as short as possible.
- The output decoupling capacitor should be connected with very short leads to the output and ground leads of the ZN414.
- The tuned circuit should be kept as far away as possible from the battery and from the loudspeaker and leads connecting these components to the circuit.
- The "earthy" side of the tuning capacitor (the moving part) must be connected to the junction of the feedback resistor and the second decoupling capacitor.

A basic radio circuit using a minimum of components is shown in Fig. 5-1. L1 and C1 is a conventional tuned circuit, e.g., a high-Q proprietary coil on a ferrite rod with a matching value of tuning capacitor. Alternatively, L1 can be made by winding approximately 80 turns of 0.3 mm diameter (30 swg) enamelled copper wire on a ferrite rod 4 cm (1 1/2 in) to 7.5 cm (3 in) long. In this case a matching value of C1 is 150 pF.

This circuit will provide sufficient output power for driving a sensitive low impedance earpiece with an equivalent resistance of approximately 500 Ω. To work a high impedance crystal earpiece an additional stage of amplification is needed. This modified circuit is shown in Fig. 5-2, requiring four more resistors, a potentiometer, another capacitor and a ZTX300 transistor (or equivalent). The potentiometer R4 and resistor R5 provide volume control (by adjustment of R4). This can be omitted if the receiver is to be brought down to minimum size, as the directional effects of the ferrite rod aerial will normally provide all the volume control necessary. In that case, replace R4 and R5 with a single 270-Ω resistor.

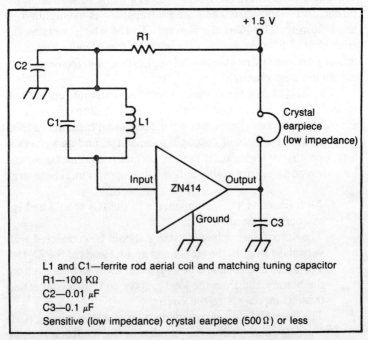

L1 and C1—ferrite rod aerial coil and matching tuning capacitor
R1—100 KΩ
C2—0.01 μF
C3—0.1 μF
Sensitive (low impedance) crystal earpiece (500 Ω) or less

Fig. 5-1. The ZN414 integrated circuit consists of a preamplifier followed by three stages of *rf* amplification and finally a transistor detector. It is a "complete" radio circuit requiring a minimum of external components to work.

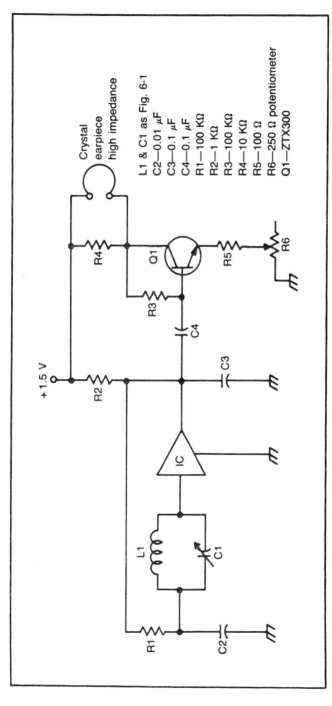

Crystal
earpiece
high impedance

L1 & C1 as Fig. 6-1
C2—0.01 μF
C3—0.1 μF
C4—0.1 μF
R1—100 KΩ
R2—1 KΩ
R3—100 KΩ
R4—10 KΩ
R5—100 Ω
R6—250 Ω potentiometer
Q1—ZTX300

Fig. 5-2. To deliver enough power to work a high impedance crystal earpiece the ZN414 is used in conjunction with an additional stage of transistor amplification. It delivers 600 mW peak output. This is the same circuit as Fig. 1-4 (Chapter 1) with the addition of a volume control (R6).

71

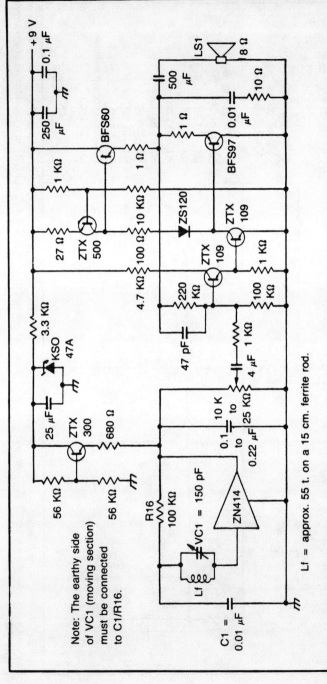

Fig. 5-3. A high quality receiver circuit based on the ZN414 integrated circuit. This is a design by Ferranti. Component values are given on the circuit diagram. A 9-volt battery is used for the supply voltage.

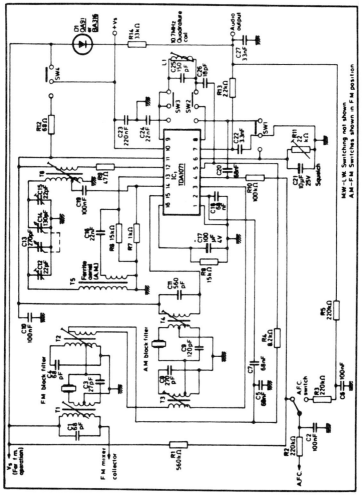

Fig. 5-4. Circuit diagram of AM/FM receiver using the TDA1071 integrated circuit (Mullard).

Table 5-1. Parts for the AM/FM Receiver Circuit.

Resistors

All resistors CR25 10%
unless stated
R1   560 KΩ
R2   220 KΩ
R3   220 KΩ
R4   8.2 KΩ
R5   220 KΩ
R6   15 KΩ
R7   1 KΩ
R8   15 KΩ
R9   47 Ω
R10   100 KΩ
R11   22 KΩ Miniature carbon preset poten-
        tiometer, Philips 2322 410 03309
R12   68 Ω
R13   2.2 KΩ
R14   33 KΩ

Capacitors

C1   68 pF
C2   100 nF
C3   27 pF
C4   68 pF
N5   68 nF
C6   100 nF
C7   68 nF
C8   270 pF
C9   120 pF
C10   100 nF
C11   560 pF
C12   22 pF
C13   270 pF*
C14   130 pF*
C15   22 pF
C16   22 nF
C17   100 μF, 4V
C18   68 nF
C19   100 nF
C20   68 nF
C21   10 μF, 25 V
C22   3.3 nF
C23   230 nF
C24   22 nF
C25   150 pF
C26   18 pF
C27   3.3 pF

*These components form part
of the ganged tuning capacitor

Winding data

T1   Primary: 12 turns, 0.071
      mm enamelled copper
      Secondary: 2 turns,
      tapped at 1 turn, 0.071
      mm enamelled copper
      Former: Toko 7P 0092

T2   Primary: 12 turns,
      tapped at 1 turn, 0.071
      mm enamelled copper
      Secondary: 3 turns,
      0.071 mm enamelled
      copper
      Former: Toko 7P 0092

T3   Primary: 3 turns, 0.071
      mm enamelled copper
      Secondary: 120 turns,
      tapped at 5 turns,
      wound over primary,
      0.071 mm enamelled
      copper
      Former: Toko 7P 0089

T4   Primary: 9 turns, tapped
      at 5 turns, 0.071 mm
      enamelled copper
      Secondary: 86 turns,
      wound over primary,
      0.071 mm enamelled
      copper
      Former: Toko 0089

T5:   M.W.—
      Primary: 78 turns,
      wound in a single layer,
      3 × 3 × 3 × 0.063 mm
      litz
      Secondary: 4 turns,
      wound over the earthy
      end of the primary 3 ×
      3 × 3 × 0.063 mm litz
      L.W.—
      Primary: 210 turns,
      wavewound, 9 × 0.063
      mm litz
      Secondary: 12 turns,
      wound under the pri-
      mary, 9 × 0.063 mm
      litz
      For T5 the coils are
      mounted on a ferrite
      rod, 178 mm in length,
      diameter 9.5 mm.

L1   8 turns, 0.071 mm
      enamelled copper.
      Former: Toko 7P 0092

Switch
SW1 to SW4 4-pole 2-way switch

Integrated circuit
IC1 TDA1071

Table 5-2. Parts for the FM Front End Circuit.

Resistors		Capacitors	
All resistors CR25 10%		C1	18 pF
R1	1.2 KΩ	C2	3.3 nF
R2	12 KΩ	C3	4.7 pF
R3	27 KΩ	C4	3.3 nF
R4	27 KΩ	C5	12 pF*
R5	12 KΩ	C6	18 pF
R6	1 KΩ	C7	3.3 nF
R7	39 Ω	C8	18 pF
R8	27 KΩ	C9	12 pF*
R9	12 KΩ	C10	3.3 nF
R10	100 Ω	C11	2.7 pF
R11	10 Ω	C12	5.6 pF
R 1-		C13	3.3 nF
2	1 kΩ	C14	56 pF
R 1-		C15	3.3 nF
3	39 Ω	C16	22 nF

Winding data

T1   Primary: 2 turns, 0.031 mm enamelled copper
      Secondary: 2 turns, 0.031 mm enamelled copper
      Former: Neosid 5 mm with ferrite core

T2   Primary: 4 turns, spaced one diameter 0.71 mm enamelled copper
      Secondary: 1 turn, interwound with the primary 0.71 mm enamelled copper
      Former: Neosid 5 mm with ferrite core

L1   3 turns, spaced one diameter and tapped at 1 1/2 turns, 0.71 mm enamelled copper
      Former: Neosid 5 mm with ferrite core

Transistors
TR1, TR2, TR3   BF195

Diode
D1   BB110

*These components form part of the ganged tuning capacitor

Fig. 5-3 shows the circuit extended to give a performance comparable to that of most domestic portable transistor receivers, driving an 8-Ω loudspeaker and powered by a 9-volt battery. This circuit does use six additional transistors and a number of other compo-

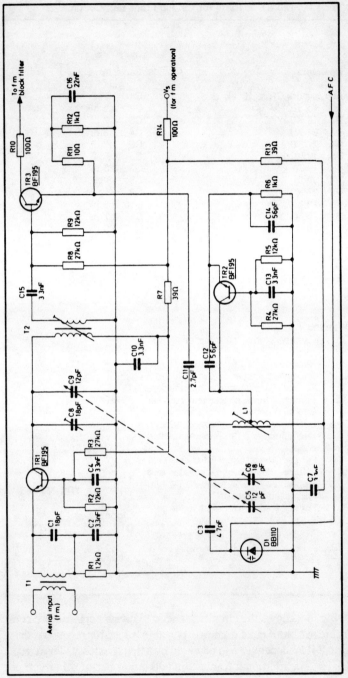

Fig. 5-5. Front-end circuit for FM operation of the receiver given in Fig. 5-4 (Mullard).

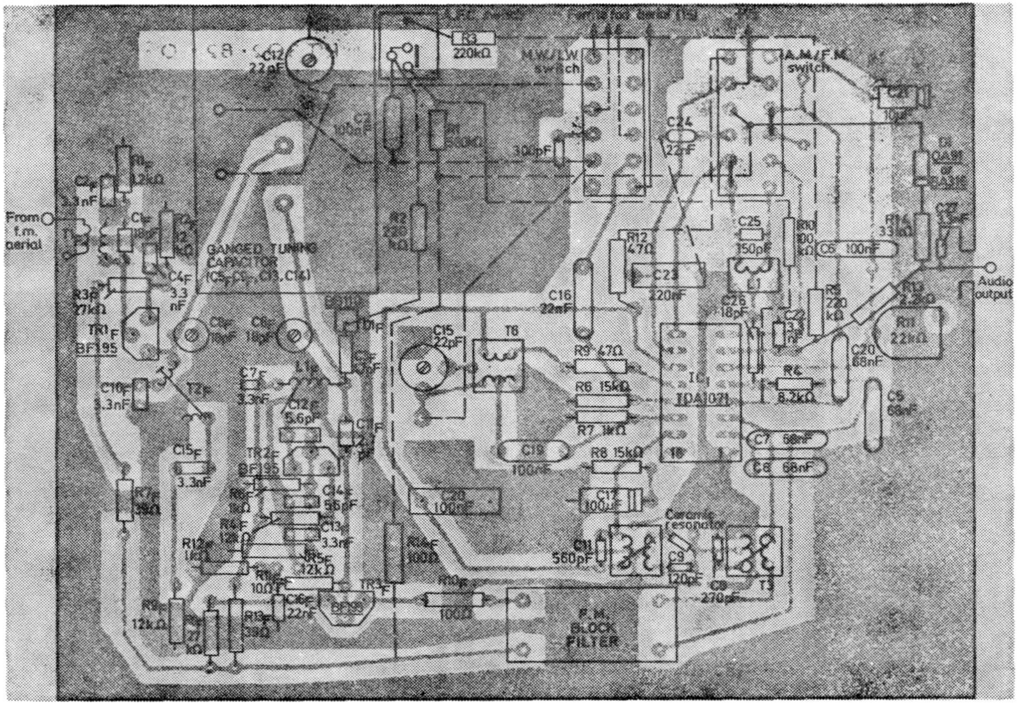

Fig. 5-6. Printed circuit layout and component positions for constructing the circuits of Figs. 5-4 and 5-5.

nents, but the component count (and cost) is still substantially less than that of an all-transistor receiver of comparable quality (it is the equivalent of a 16 transistor set).

AM/FM RADIOS

A design for a high performance AM/FM radio receiver is shown in Figs. 5-4 and 5-5. These circuits are by Mullard and are based on their TDA 1071 integrated circuit which incorporates an AM oscillator, an AM mixer with *agc*, a four-stage differential amplifier and limiter and a four-quadrant multiplier. Both AM and FM functions are combined in the multiplier, giving symmetrical demodulation on AM and quadrative detection with squelch on FM.

Figure 5-4 shows the AM circuit, working from a ferrite rod aerial. Figure 5-5 shows the circuit for the additional front-end required for FM working, connected to an FM aerial. These circuits will work on any battery voltage from 4.5 volts to 9 volts. For FM operation, the AM-FM switch (SW4) moved to the FM position switches off the AM mixer and oscillator and brings the FM front-end circuit into operation. The squelch circuit is separately controlled by SW1, the threshold of squelch operation being set by the potentiometer R11 in Fig. 5-4.

Component values are given on the two circuit diagrams. A complete list is also given in Tables 5-1 and 5-2.

Figure 5-6 shows a printed circuit layout for the complete circuits of Figs. 5-4 and 5-5, using the components specified. Components with the subscript F are those in the front end circuit (Fig. 5-5). One additional component is also shown—a 300 pF capacitor adjacent to the medium wave/long wave AM aerial switch, which does not appear on the relevant circuit diagram (Fig. 5-4).

Note also that this circuit is complete only up to the audio output stage—i.e., it needs to be followed by an audio amplifier and speaker(s)—see Chapter 4 for possible circuits to use.

Chapter 6

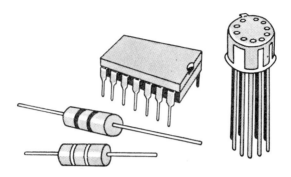

Multivibrators

The simplest form of IC multivibrator merely uses an op-amp in a basic oscillator circuit such as that shown in Fig. 6-1. Oscillation frequency will depend on the IC parameter and the values of the external resistors. The components shown give an output frequency of 1 kHz in the form of a square wave.

The addition of a diode to this circuit, as in Fig. 6-2, provides a simple *pulse generator* circuit where the pulse width can be adjusted by using different values for R2. The value of resistor R3 governs the actual pulse duration.

An alternative form of multivibrator is to use two op-amps connected as cross-coupled inverting amplifiers, as shown in Fig. 6-3. Here the frequency is established by the time constants of the RC combinations R1-C1 and R2-C2. R1 and R2 should be the same value, and can be anything from 1 KΩ to 10 KΩ. C1 and C2 should also be similar values, and anything from 0.01 to 10 μF can be used. The basic rules governing adjustment and oscillation frequency are that for any particular value of R1 and R2, *increasing* the value of C1 and C2 will *decrease* the oscillation frequency, and vice versa. Similarly, for any particular value of C1 and C2 *decreasing* the value of R1 and R2 will *increase* the frequency, and vice versa.

With the component values shown, i.e., R1 = R2 = 8.2 KΩ and C1 = C2 = 0.2 μF, the oscillation frequency will be 1 kHz. Decreasing the value of R1 and R2 to 1 KΩ should result in an oscillation frequency of 10 kHz.

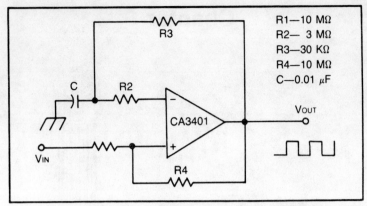

Fig. 6-1. Simple multivibrator (or square wave oscillator) circuit based on the CK3401 op-amp. Component values may be chosen to give any specific output frequency required, within limits. These component values give a 1 kHz square wave output.

A rather more versatile multivibrator circuit is shown in Fig. 6-4, which has independent controls of "on" and "off" periods. The frequency range is adjustable by choice of capacitor C1 which governs the duration of the square wave pulse generated, viz:

Value of C1	pulse period	frequency
1 μF	4 min to 1 sec	250-1 Hz
0.1 μF	0.4 min to 100 min	2500-600 Hz
0.01 μF	4 min to 10 min	1500-6000 Hz
0.00 μF	4 sec to 1 min	15000 kHz-60 kHz

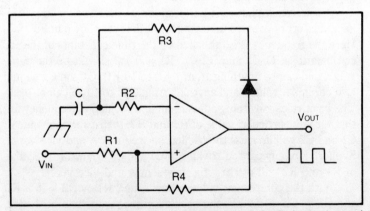

Fig. 6-2. An almost identical circuit, with the addition of a diode, can be used as a pulse generator. Here the value of R3 determines the pulse duration and the value of R2 determines the "off" period.

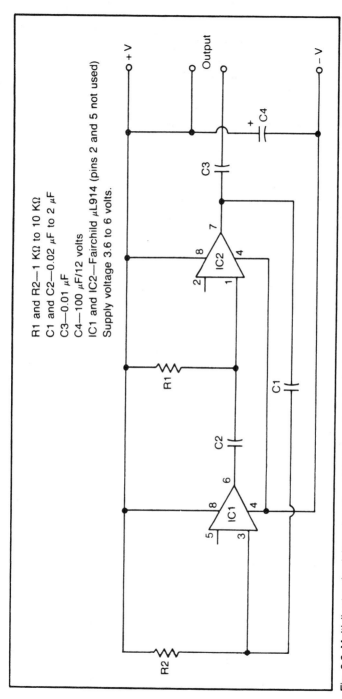

R1 and R2—1 KΩ to 10 KΩ
C1 and C2—0.02 μF to 2 μF
C3—0.01 μF
C4—100 μF/12 volts
IC1 and IC2—Fairchild μL914 (pins 2 and 5 not used)
Supply voltage 3.6 to 6 volts.

Fig. 6-3. Multivibrator circuit based on the μL914 integrated circuit which is basically two inverting op-amps. The frequency of oscillation is determined by the time constants of R1, C2 and R2.

81

Adjustment of "on" and "off" times of oscillation within these ranges is governed by the potentiometers R4 and R5.

Another multivibrator circuit is shown in Fig. 6-5, which is particularly notable for its stable performance. The frequency of oscillation is maintained to within plus or minus 2 percent on any supply voltage from 6 to 15 volts and is independent of the actual voltage. It uses a CA3094 op-amp IC with external resistors and one capacitor. The circuit also includes a lamp which flashes on and off at a rate of one flash per second with the component values given.

Flashing rate can be adjusted by altering the values of R1 and R2 and/or C. To adjust values to give any required flashing rate (frequency), the following formula applies:

$$\text{frequency} = \frac{1}{2RC1_n(2R1/R2 + 1)}$$

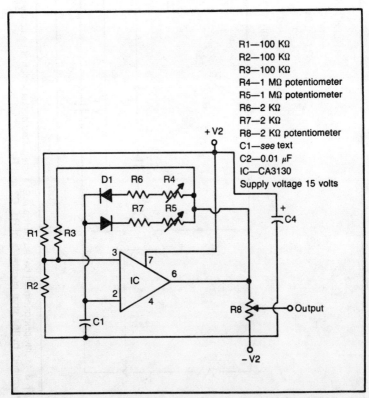

R1—100 KΩ
R2—100 KΩ
R3—100 KΩ
R4—1 MΩ potentiometer
R5—1 MΩ potentiometer
R6—2 KΩ
R7—2 KΩ
R8—2 KΩ potentiometer
C1—*see* text
C2—0.01 μF
IC—CA3130
Supply voltage 15 volts

Fig. 6-4. Multivibrator circuit with adjustable "on" and "off" periods.

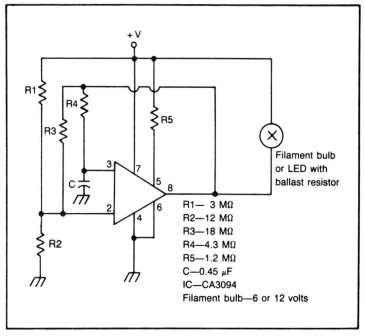

Fig. 6-5. Astable multivibrator with low frequency of duration to work a flashing light. Component values given provide a flashing rate of about 1 per second working off a 6 to 15 volt battery.

$$\text{where } R = \frac{R1 \bullet R2}{R1 + R2}$$

In a variation on this circuit shown in Fig. 6-6, the introduction of a potentiometer R2 enables the pulse length to be varied while maintaining a constant frequency (pulse repetition rate). Again this circuit can be used to flash a filament lamp, or a light emitting diode. In the latter case, a ballast resistor is needed in series with the LED.

Another straightforward free-running multivibrator is shown in Fig. 6-7, using a CA3094 integrated circuit. The frequency is controlled by the value selected for R3, and so using a potentiometer for this component enables the frequency to be adjusted. The frequency is also dependent on the supply voltage, which can be anything from 3 volts up to 12 volts.

Designing a multivibrator circuit to work at an audio frequency, while retaining adjustment of frequency, forms the basis of a *metronome*. The only additional circuitry required is a simple low-power audio amplifier of the kind described in Chapter 4, connecting to a loudspeaker.

TIMER CIRCUITS

A number of ICs have been developed specifically for multivibrator applications. These are called timer ICs. They make the design of monostable (one shot) and astable (free running) multivibrator circuits quite easy.

Without a doubt, the most popular timer IC is the 555. This easy to use 8 pin chip is extremely versatile.

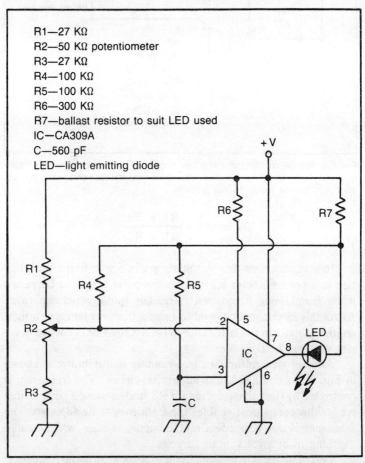

R1—27 KΩ
R2—50 KΩ potentiometer
R3—27 KΩ
R4—100 KΩ
R5—100 KΩ
R6—300 KΩ
R7—ballast resistor to suit LED used
IC—CA309A
C—560 pF
LED—light emitting diode

Fig. 6-6. Adjustable multivibrator circuit, potentiometer R2 varying the pulse width, or "on" time of the LED indicator. Flashing rate is approximately 1 per second. Supply voltage required for this circuit is 22 to 30 volts.

84

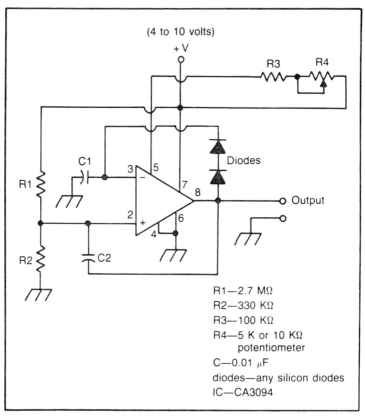

Fig. 6-7. Free running multivibrator (or pule generator) circuit, the frequency of which can be varied by adjustment of the potentiometer R4.

The basic 555 monostable multivibrator circuit is illustrated in Fig. 6-8. Notice how simple this circuit is — just three external components (two capacitors and a resistor).

Capacitor C2 helps stabilize the circuit. It is not needed in all cases, but it doesn't hurt to include it. A small disc capacitor (0.001 μF to 0.01 μF) will do the job just fine, and will not add appreciably to the component cost.

The length of the output pulse is determined by R1 and C1. When a trigger pulse is received, the output goes high for a time equal to;

$$T = 1.1R1C1$$

where T is the time in seconds, R1 is in Ω, and C1 is in farads.

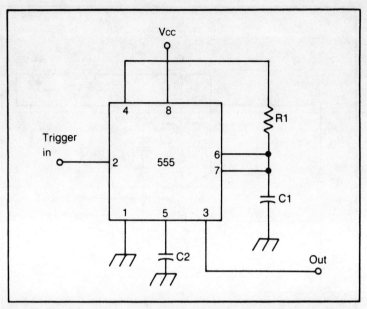

Fig. 6-8. The 555 timer IC is the heart of many simple monostable multivibrator circuits.

For example, if R1 is 220k, and C1 is 0.1 μF, the length of the output pulse will be;

$$T = 1.1 \times 220000 \times 0.0000001 = 0.0242 \text{ second}$$

For practical designs, we will generally need to know the component values for a specific time period. In most cases it is easiest to select a likely value for C1, and then rearrange the equation to solve for R1;

$$R1 = T/1.1C1$$

As an example, let's say we need an output pulse of 0.5 second. If we use a 0.5 μF capacitor for C1, we need a resistance of;

$$R1 = 0.5/(1.1 \times 0.0000005) = 0.5/0.00000055 = 909,091 \ \Omega$$

A 910 K resistor could be used.

The basic 555 timer astable multivibrator circuit is quite similar. It is shown in Fig. 6-9. The primary differences are that there is no trigger input, and a second timing resistor (R2) has been added to the circuit.

The time the output is in its high state is determined by both resistors, and capacitor C1;

$$Th = 0.693(R1 + R2)C1$$

while, the output low time is controlled by just R2 and C1;

$$Tl = 0.693R2C1$$

Notice that the output high time must always be at least slightly

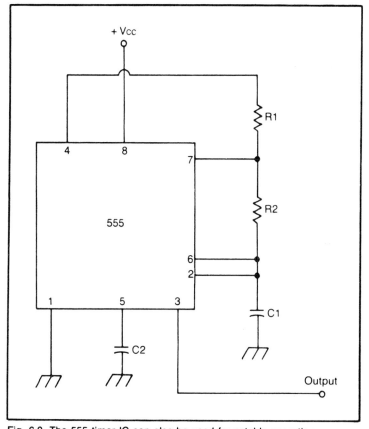

Fig. 6-9. The 555 timer IC can also be used for astable operation.

longer than the output low time.

The total output cycle time is simply the sum of the high and low times;

$$Tt = Th + Tl$$

If we combine the equations, we get;

$$Tt = 0.693(R1 + 2R2)C1$$

Before moving on, let's look at a couple of practical examples. For our first example, let's assume the following component values;

$$R1 = 10K$$
$$R2 = 10K$$
$$C1 = 1 \mu F$$

In this case, the output high time works out to;

$$Th = 0.693(10000 + 10000) \times 0.000001 =$$
$$0.0693 \times 20000 \times 0.000001 =$$
$$0.01386 \text{ second}$$

The output low time is;

$$Tl = 0.693 \times 10000 \times 0.000001 =$$
$$0.00693 \text{ second}$$

The total cycle time is simply the sum of these two values;

$$Tt = 0.01386 + 0.00693 =$$
$$0.02079 \text{ second}$$

Or, using the combined equation;

$$Tt = 0.693(10000 + (2 \times 10000)) \times 0.000001 =$$
$$0.693(10000 + 20000) \times 0.000001 =$$
$$0.693 \times 30000 \times 0.000001 =$$
$$0.02079 \text{ second}$$

Notice that we get the same results in both cases.

For our second example, we will assume the following compo-nent values;

$$R1 = 10K$$
$$R2 = 100K$$
$$C1 = 50 \ \mu F$$

This time, the high time equals;

$$Th = 0.693(10000 + 100000) \times 0.00005 =$$
$$0.693 \times 110000 \times 0.00005 =$$
$$3.8115 \text{ seconds}$$

And the low time is;

$$Tl = 0.693 \times 100000 \times 0.00005 =$$
$$3.465 \text{ seconds}$$

So the total cycle time works out to;

$$Tt = 3.8115 + 3.465 =$$
$$7.2765 \text{ seconds}$$

These examples clearly indicate that the 555 can be used for a wide range of time periods.

In most practical astable applications, we are more concerned with the output frequency than cycle time. The frequency is sim-ply the reciprocal of the total cycle time;

$$F = 1/Tt$$

For our two examples, we get frequencies of;

$$F = 1/0.02079 =$$
$$48 \text{ Hz. (appx.)}$$

and;

$$F = 1/72.765 =$$
$$0.0137 \text{ Hz. (appx.)}$$

Notice that larger cycle times result in lower frequencies.

We can calculate the frequency directly by using this formula;

$$F = 1.44/((R1 + 2R2)C1)$$

As an example, let's consider the following component values;

$$R1 = 22K$$
$$R2 = 33K$$
$$C1 = 0.01 \ \mu F$$

Here, the output frequency works out to approximately;

$$F = 1.44/((22000 + (2 \times 33000)) \times 0.00000001) =$$
$$1.44/((22000 + 66000) \times 0.00000001) =$$
$$1.44/(88000 \times 0.00000001) =$$
$$1.44/0.00088 =$$
$$1636 \ Hz.$$

In most practical applications, we will need to find the component values that will provide the desired output frequency. There are two approaches you could take.

The first approach would be to select the resistor values first for the desired duty cycle, then rearrange the equation to solve for C1;

$$C1 = 1.44/((R1 + 2R2) \times F)$$

For example, let's say we need a 100 Hz signal with a 1:3 duty cycle. The duty cycle ratio is;

$$R2 : R1 + R2$$

R2, by definition, is equal to 1 in the ratio. We simply select a likely value — say, 10K, then factor the duty cycle ratio;

$$1 : 3$$
$$1r : Xr + 1r$$

In this example, R1 should be twice the value of R2, or 20K. If we assume our application is not overly critical, we can simply use the nearest standard resistance value, which is 22K.

Now, we just plug the values into the rearranged frequency equation;

$$C1 = 1.44/((10000 + (2 \times 22000)) \times 100) =$$
$$1.44/((10000 + 44000) \times 100) =$$
$$1.44/(54000 \times 100) =$$
$$1.44/5400000 =$$
$$0.00000027 \text{ farad} =$$
$$0.27 \ \mu F$$

A 0.25 μF, or a 0.3 μF capacitor would probably do, but in some applications you will need some rather oddball capacitance values. You can usually make do with series and/or parallel combinations of standard capacitance values.

The other method of solving for component values is to select a likely value for C1, then solve for the lumped resistance R, which is equal to (R1 + 2R2). This time the equation looks like this;

$$R = 1.44/(C1 \times F)$$

Again we will assume we need a 100 Hz output with a 1:3 duty cycle. For the time being, we will ignore the duty cycle, and just solve for R.

A 0.1 μF capacitor would be a reasonable choice, so;

$$R = 1.44/(0.0000001 \times 100) =$$
$$1.44/0.00001 =$$
$$144,000 \ \Omega$$

Now we know that;

$$R = 144,000 = R1 + 2R2$$

The next step is to factor the duty cycle as described above. For a 1:3 duty cycle, R1 should be twice the value of R2, so we can easily find the value of R2;

$$R = 144000 = R1 + 2R2 =$$
$$2R2 + 2R2 =$$
$$4R2$$
$$R2 = 144000/4 =$$
$$36000 \ \Omega$$

R1 is simply twice the value of R2, so;

$$R1 = 2R2 =$$
$$2 \times 36000 =$$
$$72000 \ \Omega$$

These aren't standard resistance values. You could use parallel/series combinations of standard resistance values, or you could use trimpots for R1 and R2.

If your application is not too critical you could round the values off. For example, you could use a 33K resistor for R2 and a 68K resistor for R1. The actual output frequency would work out to;

$$F = 1.44/((68000 + (2 \times 33000)) \times 0.0000001) =$$
$$1.44/((68000 + 66000) \times 0.0000001) =$$
$$1.44/(134000 \times 0.0000001) =$$
$$1.44/0.0134 =$$
$$107 \ Hz.$$

That's pretty close to the desired frequency of 100 Hz. Component tolerances could create that much error, so the rounding off effect is minimal, except in very critical applications using low tolerance components.

PROGRAMMABLE TIMERS

555 timer circuits are ideal for many monostable and astable timing applications in which fixed timing periods are required. However, they aren't so suitable for applications in which the timing period must be changed, or when multiple time periods are simultaneously required.

The timing resistor in a monostable circuit could be replaced with a potentiometer. Also, several timing capacitors could be selected via a switch to set the operating range.

Variable frequency astable circuits have additional problems. One or both of the timing resistors could be replaced with potentiometers, but unless both resistances are changed in exact unison, the duty cycle will vary as the frequency is changed. Switch selectable timing capacitors could be used, but this is still a bit awkward.

The solution is a programmable timer, such as the XR-2240. The pin-out diagram for this powerful and versatile IC is shown in Fig. 6-10. This chip has eight outputs in a binary weighted scheme.

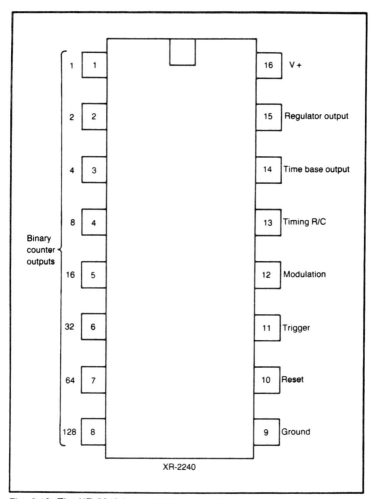

Fig. 6-10. The XR-2240 is a programmable timer integrated circuit.

The basic timing period is determined by a single resistor and capacitor. The formula is as simple as it can possibly be — even simpler than the one for the 555 timer;

$$T = RC$$

A timing pulse equal to T is available at pin #1. A timing pulse twice the basic timing period (2T) is brought out to pin #2. The output at pin #3 has twice the timing period of pin #2 (4T). This pattern is continued to pin #8, with each pin outputting a timing period twice that of its predecessor;

pin #1	T
pin #2	2T
pin #3	4T
pin #4	8T
pin #5	16T
pin #6	32T
pin #7	64T
pin #8	128T

If an intermediate value is required, two or more pins can be tied together. For example, if we need a timing pulse of 21T, we would tie the following pins together;

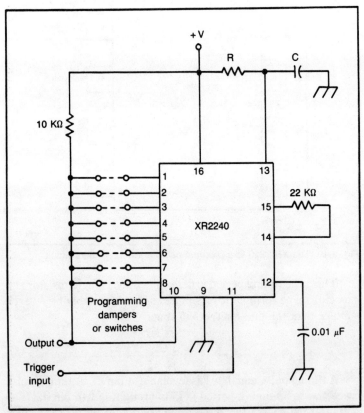

Fig. 6-11. This is the basic programmable monostable multivibrator circuit built around the XR2240.

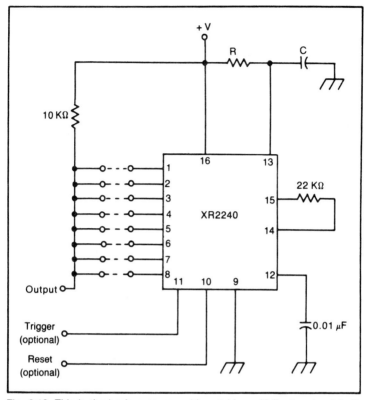

Fig. 6-12. This is the basic programmable astable multivibrator circuit built around the XR-2240.

pin #5	16T
pin #3	4T
pin #1	1T
total	21T

The basic monostable circuit built around the XR-2240 is shown in Fig. 6-11.

The astable circuit, shown in Fig. 6-12, is quite similar.

In either circuit, a string of 8 DIP switches can be used to select any time value from 1T to 255T.

Chapter 7

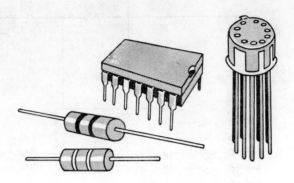

Voltage Regulators

Where a semiconductor circuit operating on low voltage *dc* is powered from the mains supply via a step-down transformer, voltage regulation is highly desirable in many circuits in order to ensure constant *dc* supply voltage. This can be provided by using zener diodes in associated circuitry. Exactly the same function can be performed by a single IC. A particular advantage is that such an IC can also incorporate internal overload and short-circuit protection which would call for numerous extra components in a circuit using discrete components.

A typical circuit is shown in Fig. 7-1, giving a rectified, positive *dc* voltage output from the center tapped secondary of the transformer. The same components can be used in mirror-image configuration to give a negative output voltage from the center tap (in which case the polarity of the two electrolytic capacitors must be reversed).

Performance characteristics of a family of ICs designed as voltage regulators are given in Fig. 7-2. They are quite small devices in a TO-39 metal case with three leads—input, output and earth. The earth or ground lead is internally connected to the case.

A circuit similar to that in Fig. 7-1, which uses the TBA435 chip is shown in Fig. 7-3.

There are numerous other simple voltage regulators which can be built from integrated circuit arrays (*see* Chapter 2) simply by "tapping" the appropriate leads to connect the individual compo-

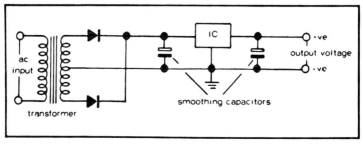

Fig. 7-1. Typical circuit for stepping down an ac voltage via a transformer and rectifying it to produce a lower dc output.

nents required into the complete circuit. An example is shown in Fig. 7-4, which is a regulator to provide an adjustable constant voltage *dc* output from an unregulated (and thus possibly variable) 20 volt *dc* input. It uses the transistors, diode and zener diode contained in the CA 3097E chip with a potentiometer and external resistor to complete the circuit. The actual output voltage can be adjusted from 9.5 to 15 volts by the setting of the potentiometer, with an output current ranging up to 40 mA, depending on the value of the output load.

Other simple voltage regulators can be based on op-amps. A basic circuit is shown in Fig. 7-5. The reference voltage is set by the zener diode, the value of R1 being chosen to provide optimum zener current for the input voltage concerned. The (regulated) out-

IC type no.	input voltage	output voltage	Max. output current
TBA 435	20	8.5	200 mA
TBA 625A	20	5	200 mA
TBA 625B	27	12	200 mA
TBA 625C	27	15	200 mA

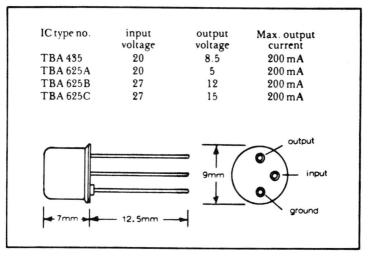

Fig. 7-2. TBA435 integrated circuit is enclosed in a TO-39 metal can shape and looks like a transistor because it only has three leads.

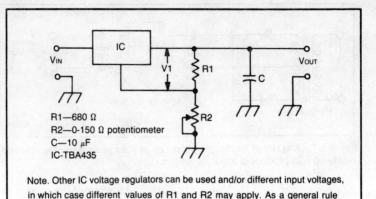

Fig. 7-3. Adjustable output voltage regulator circuit. The potential divider formed by R1 and R2 following the IC enables the output voltage to be adjusted via R2; otherwise the circuit is the same as Fig. 7-1. Alternatively this circuit can be applied to a *dc* input:

$$V_{OUT} = V1 \left(1 + \frac{R2}{R1} + 1_G R2\right)$$

Component values for this circuit with an input voltage of 18 volts are given in the figure.

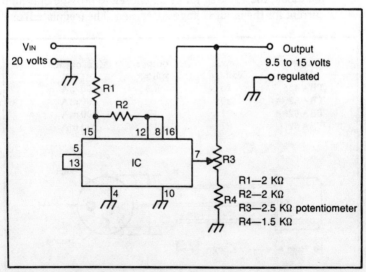

Fig. 7-4. Voltage regulator using the CA3097E integrated circuit array. This provides 9.5 to 15 volts regulated output from a 20 volts *dc* input, the actual output voltage being determined by the setting of R3.

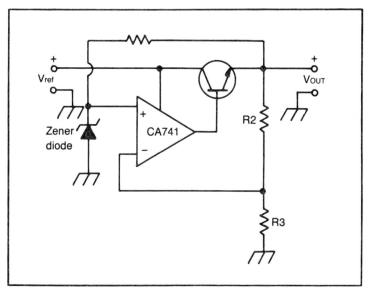

Fig. 7-5. Simple voltage regulator circuit using an op-amp and a zener diode to set the regulated voltage. The values of resistors R2 and R3 determine the output voltage (see text).

put voltage is determined by the reference voltage (V ref) and the values of R2 and R3:

$$V_{OUT} = V \text{ ref} \left(\frac{R2 + R3}{R3} \right)$$

A circuit which provides a small difference between *volts in* and *volts out* is shown in Fig. 7-6. Using a PNP transistor it needs only about 1 volt to saturate the transistor, while adequate current is available for the regulating circuit using an NPN transistor. The same circuit would need about 4 volts difference between input and output to maintain regulation.

With the circuit shown in Fig. 8-6,

$$V_{OUT} = 1.6 \frac{(R1 + R2)}{R1}$$

Another very useful circuit is shown in Fig. 7-7, which provides a split supply from a single battery source. In other words it halves the input voltage while also producing a good degree of regulation

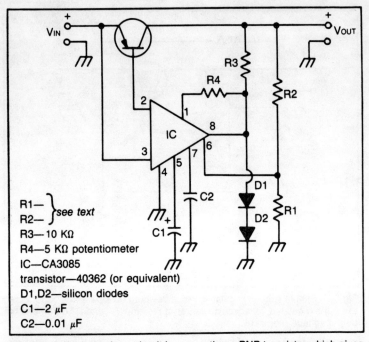

Fig. 7-6. Voltage regulator circuit incorporating a PNP transistor which gives a difference between Vᴵɴ and Vᴏᴜᴛ of about 1 volt (i.e., the voltage necessary to saturate the transistor).

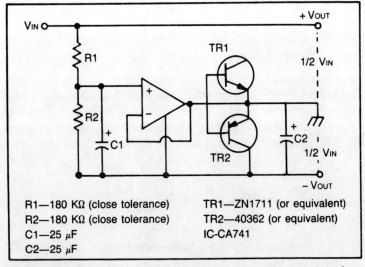

Fig. 7-7. This circuit gives a regulated split supply from any input voltage from 5 to 36 volts.

of the two (plus and minus) voltage outputs. None of the component values is critical but R1 and R2 should be of close-tolerance type of equal value. Input voltage can range from 6 to 36 volts, when one half of the input voltage will appear between output + and 0, and the other between 0 and output – .

Chapter 8

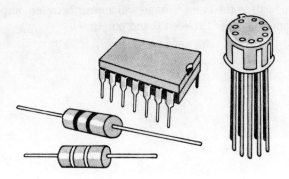

Electric Motor Speed Controllers

A variety of ICs are designed as speed regulators for small *dc* motors such as those used in portable cassette players, movie cameras, models and toys. The object is to "govern" the motor so that it runs at a constant speed, independent of variations in battery supply voltage and load on the motor. The TDA1151 is selected for the following circuits, having a maximum rating of 20 volts (which covers most model and other small *dc* motors), with an output current of up to 800 milliamps. It is a flat rectangular plastic package with three leads emerging from one end, and comprises 18 transistors, 4 diodes and 7 resistors in a linear integrated circuit.

In its simplest application it is used with a potentiometer (R_s) acting as a speed regulation resistance (and by which the actual motor speed is adjusted); and a torque control resistor (R_t)which provides automatic regulation against load on the motor. Both these resistors are bridged by capacitors, although C2 can be omitted—*see* Fig. 8-1. Component values shown are suitable for a 6 to 12 volt supply.

A slightly different circuit is shown in Fig. 8-2, using a TCA600/900 or TCA610/910 integrated circuit. These have maximum voltage ratings of 14 and 20 volts respectively; and maximum current ratings of 400 milliamps for starting, but only 140 milliamps for continuous running.

Devices of this type work on the principle of providing a constant output voltage to the motor independent of variations of sup-

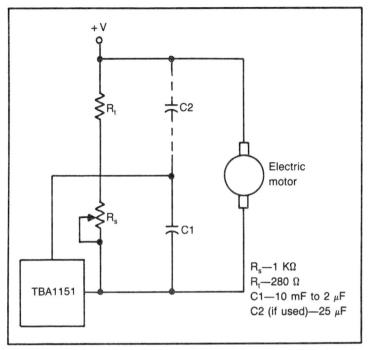

Fig. 8-1. Use of the TDA1151 linear integrated circuit as a speed regulator for a small *dc* electric motor.

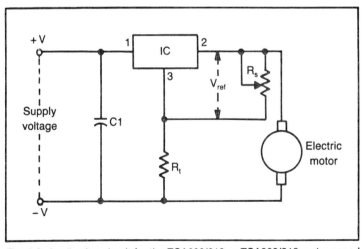

Fig. 8-2. Application circuit for the TCA600/610 or TCA900/910 motor speed regulators. R_s is the speed regulation resistor (variable). R_t is the torque control resistor. A suitable value for C1 is 0.1 F. A diode can be added in line 3 to provide temperature compensation as well.

ply voltage, the value of this voltage being set by adjustment of R_s. At the same time the device can generate a negative output resistance to compensate speed fluctuations due to variations in torque. This negative output resistance is equal to RT/K, where K is a constant, depending on the parameters of the device, viz:

IC	K (typical)	Vref	I_o
TDA1151	20	1.2	1.7 mA
TCA600/900	8.5	2.6	2.6 mA
TCA610/910	8.5	2.6	2.6 mA

The above also shows the reference voltage (Vref) and quiescent current drain (I_o) of the three ICs mentioned.

The following relationships then apply for calculating suitable component values for these circuits:

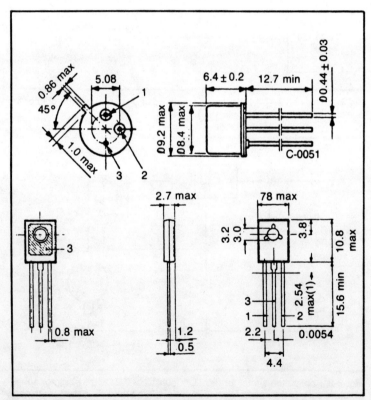

Fig. 8-3. Physical appearance of the TCA600/610 in a TO-39 metal can and the TCA900/910 in a flat plastic package.

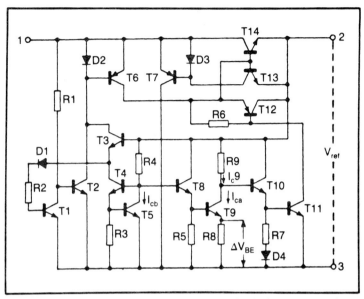

Fig. 8-4. Although small devices, these integrated circuits for motor speed control are based on the complicated circuitry shown here.

$$R_t = K \cdot R_M$$

where R_M is the typical motor resistance.

$$\text{Minimum value of Rs} = \frac{\text{Vref} \cdot \text{RT}}{\text{Eg} - (\text{Vref} - 1_o\text{RT})}$$

where Eg = back *emf* of motor at required or rated speed, and I_o = quiescent current drain of the device.

Actual voltage developed across the motor is given by:

$$\text{Volts (at motor)} = R_M \cdot I_M + \text{Eg}$$

where I_M is the current drain by the motor at required or rated speed.

The physical appearance of these chips can be seen in Fig. 8-3, while Fig. 8-4 shows the complex internal circuitry within one of these chips.

Chapter 9

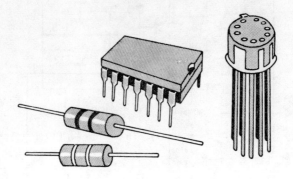

Filters

A basic filter circuit consists of a combination of a resistor and a capacitor. This combination of R and C has a *time constant* which defines the *cut-off frequency* of the filter; but the actual mode of working also depends on the configuration of the two components (see Fig. 9-1.)

With R in series and C across the circuit, frequencies *lower* than the cut-off frequency are passed without attenuation. Frequencies at above the cut-off frequency are then sharply attenuated. This is called a *low-pass filter*.

With C in series and R across the circuit, frequencies *above* the cut-off frequency are passed without attenuations. Frequencies below the cut-off frequency are then sharply attenuated. This is called a *high-pass filter*. Practical circuits for these two types of filter are shown in Fig. 9-2.

The amount of attenuation provided by a filter is expressed by the ratio volts out/volts in, or voltage ratio. This is quoted in decibels (dB)—a 3dB drop being equivalent to a voltage ratio drop from 1.0 to 0.707, or a *power* loss of 50 percent.

Op-amps can be used as practical filters associated with an external capacitor, with the advantage that the more sophisticated circuitry involved can provide superior performance to straightforward RC combinations.

Two filter circuits based on the CA301 op-amp are shown in Fig. 9-2. In the case of the low-pass filter component values are

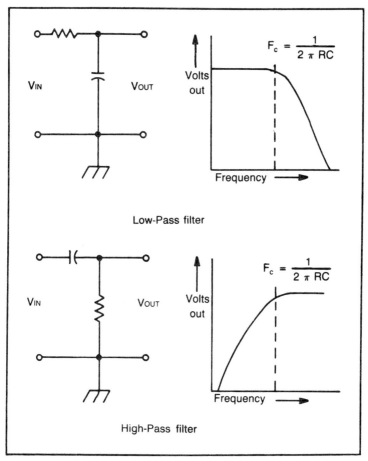

Fig. 9-1. Basic filters are provided by a combination of resistor (R) and capacitor (C). A low pass filter attenuates frequencies above the critical frequency (f_c). A high pass filter attenuates frequencies below f_C.

calculated from these formulas:

$$C1 = \frac{R1 + R2}{1.414R1R2f_c}$$

$$C2 = \frac{1.414}{(R1 + R2)\, f_c}$$

where f_c is the effective cut-off point.

107

In the case of the high-pass filter circuit:

$$C1 = \frac{R1 + R2}{1.732 R1 R2\ f_c}$$

$$C2 = \frac{1.732}{(R1 + R2)\ f_c}$$

Bandpass filters or bandwidth filters can be produced by combining a low-pass filter in series with a high-pass filter. If the band-

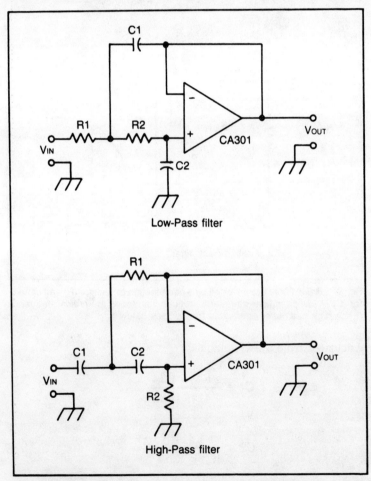

Fig. 9-2. Basic low-pass and high-pass filter circuits incorporating an op-amp for better performance.

108

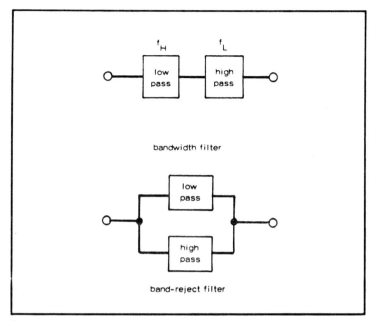

Fig. 9-3. A low-pass filter in series with a high-pass filter passes frequencies only within the bandwidth f_L-f_H. A low-pass filter in parallel with a high-pass filter rejects all frequencies within the bandwidth f_L-f_H.

width is from f_L to f_H, then the cut-off frequency for the low-pass filter is made f_H and that of the high-pass filter f_L—Fig. 9-3 (top). This filter combination will pass frequencies from f_L to f_H, i.e., in the desired band.

To produce a *band-reject filter*, a low-pass filter is used in parallel with a high-pass filter, as in the second diagram. This combination will reject all frequencies within the band f_L to f_H.

Bandpass and band-reject filters are essentially functional mirror images of each other, as illustrated in the frequency response graphs of Fig. 9-4. For convenience, we will confine our discussion to the bandpass filter.

This type of filter has two cut-off frequencies—the upper cut-off and the lower cut-off. The action of the filter can not be described with a single specification as the low-pass and high-pass filters can.

Usually the cut-off frequencies are not identified specifically in describing bandpass filters. Instead, we identify the mid-point between the two cut-off frequencies. This is called the center frequency, for obvious reasons.

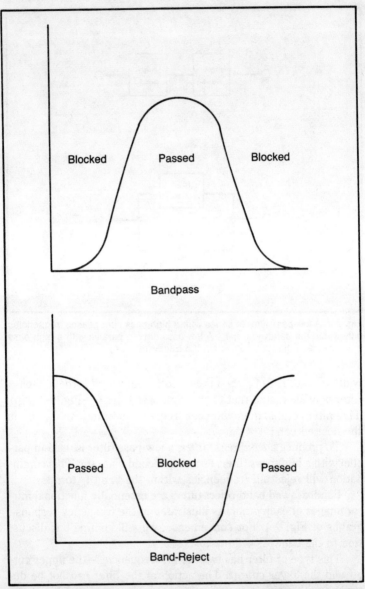

Fig. 9-4. Bandpass and band-reject filters are functional mirror images of each other.

But we still need another specification to indicate how far apart the cut-off frequencies are. This specification is generally given in one of two forms. The most direct is the bandwidth specification.

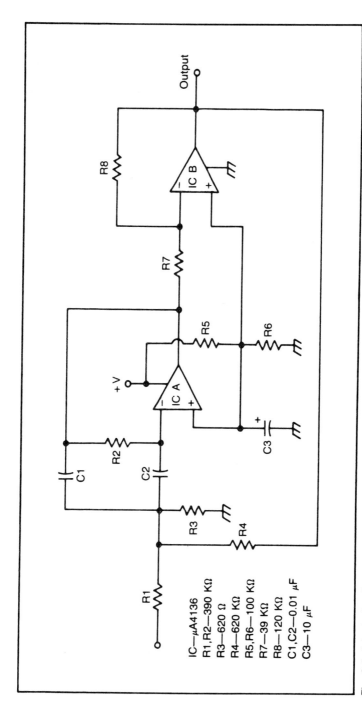

Fig. 9-5. A typical active bandpass filter.

IC—µA4136
R1,R2—390 KΩ
R3—620 Ω
R4—620 KΩ
R5,R6—100 KΩ
R7—39 KΩ
R8—120 KΩ
C1,C2—0.01 µF
C3—10 µF

111

This is simply the frequency distance from the lower cut-off to the upper cut-off.

This can all be made clearer with an example. Let's say the lower cut-off frequency is 3000 Hz, and the upper cut-off frequency is 5000 Hz. The center frequency is 4000 Hz, and the bandwidth is the difference between the cut-offs (5000 - 3000 = 2000 Hz).

More commonly, the bandwidth specification is given in terms of Q, or the Quality factor. The lower the Q, the wider the bandwidth. Q is defined as the center frequency divided by the bandwidth:

$$Q = \frac{Fc}{BW}$$

or, for our example:

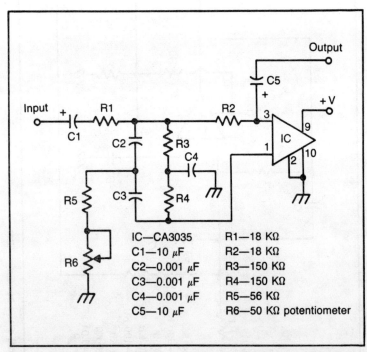

IC—CA3035	R1—18 KΩ
C1—10 μF	R2—18 KΩ
C2—0.001 μF	R3—150 KΩ
C3—0.001 μF	R4—150 KΩ
C4—0.001 μF	R5—56 KΩ
C5—10 μF	R6—50 KΩ potentiometer

Fig. 9-6. A notch filter rejects input signals at a specific center frequency but passes all other frequencies. This is a working circuit, the center frequency being determined by the value of components in the two networks R3-R4-R5-R6: and C2-C3-C4. The actual "sharpness" of rejection or notch width is adjustable via potentiometer R6. Component values for a 1 kHz center frequency are given in the figure.

112

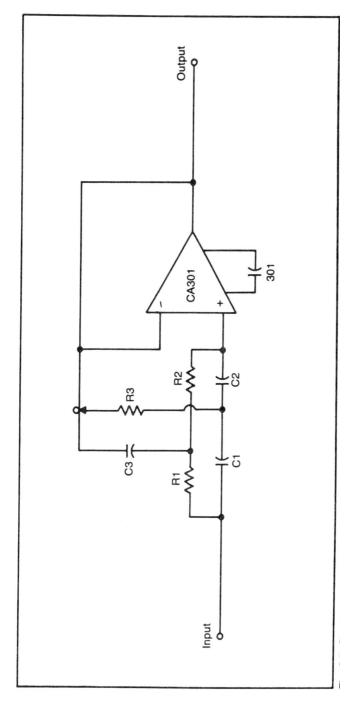

Fig. 9-7. Simple circuit for a high Q notch filter. Capacitor C1 and C2 are equal in value. Capacitor C3 = C1/2. Resistor R1 is twice the value of R2. The center frequency is $f_c = \dfrac{1}{2\pi R1C1}$.

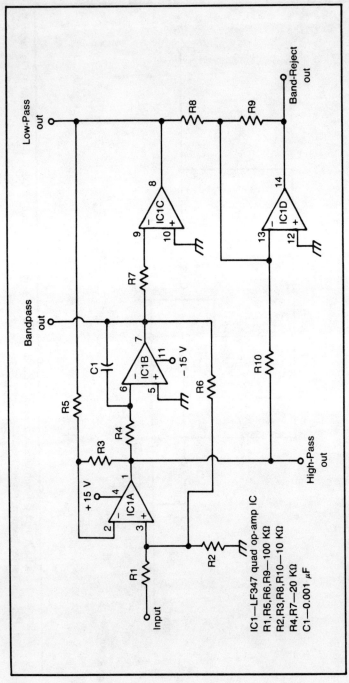

Fig. 9-8. A state variable filter features multiple filtering outputs.

114

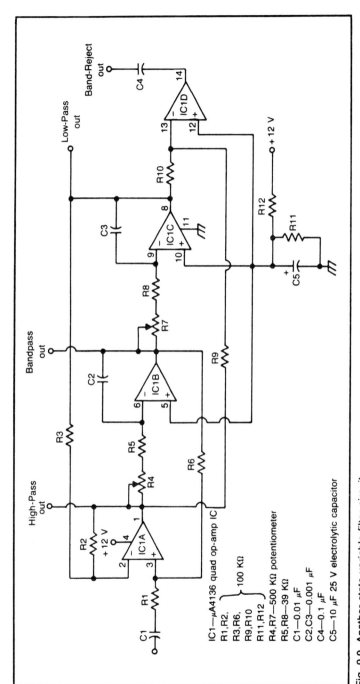

Fig. 9-9. Another state variable filter circuit.

IC1—μA4136 quad op-amp IC
R1,R2,
R3,R6,
R9,R10   } 100 KΩ
R11,R12
R4,R7—500 KΩ potentiometer
R5,R8—39 KΩ
C1—0.01 μF
C2,C3—0.001 μF
C4—0.1 μF
C5—10 μF 25 V electrolytic capacitor

115

$$Q = \frac{4000}{2000} = 2$$

A typical bandpass filter circuit is shown in Fig. 9-5. Using the component values specified, the center frequency will be about 1000 Hz.

Some practical band-reject (or notch) filter circuits are shown in Figs. 9-6 and 9-7.

There is one final type of filter of interest which we should look at before moving on. The state variable filter has multiple outputs for the various filter types described in the last few pages. A fairly typical state variable filter circuit is shown in Fig. 9-8. For the component values shown the Q is 3.4, and the cut-off frequencies for the low-pass and high-pass sections is 3000 Hz. This is also the center frequency for the bandpass section. The notch frequency is 9,500 Hz.

Figure 9-9 shows another state variable filter circuit. In this one the high-pass and low-pass cut-off frequencies are adjustable from 300 Hz to 3000 Hz. The potentiometers should have a reverse log type taper.

Chapter 10

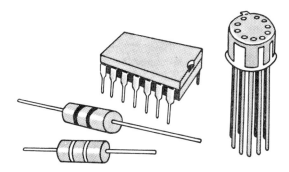

Introducing Digital Circuits

The digital system (also known as the binary system) is based on counting in 1's. Thus it has only two digits (known as "bits")—0 (zero) and 1 (one)—which are very easy to manipulate electronically. It only needs a simple on-off switch, for example, to count in this manner. The switch is either "off" (showing zero as far as the circuit is concerned) or "on" (representing a count of 1). It can continue to count in 1's, or even multiply, divide, etc, in association with other simple types of switches. The fast-as-light speed at which electronic devices can count makes the digital system very suitable for building computer circuits, particularly as only a few basic operations have to be performed. The fact that these operations, using simple logic circuits or *gates* in suitable combinations, may have to be repeated very many times is no problem either.

The decimal system expresses a number in powers of 10. In other words individual digits, depending on their order represent the digit value $\times 10^0$, digit value $\times 10^1$, digit value $\times 10^2$, etc, reading from *right to left*. Putting this the correct way round, and taking an actual number—say 124:

$$124 = 1 \times 10^2 + 2 \times 10^1 + 4 \times 10^0$$
$$= 100 + 20 + 4$$

The binary system expresses a number in powers of 2 using

only the two digits 1 and 0.

$$\begin{aligned} \text{Thus } 1011 &= 1 \times 2^3 + 0 \times 2^2 + 0 \times 2^1 + 1 \times 2^0 \\ &= 8 + 0 + 2 + 1 \\ &= 11 \end{aligned}$$

Thus a binary number is longer, written down, than its corresponding decimal number, and can get very long indeed with large decimal numbers (e.g., 10,000 = 1010100010000) but this does not matter at all as far as electronics "counting" is concerned. It only makes it difficult for people to convert decimal numbers to binary numbers, and vice versa. Here are two basic rules.

CONVERTING DECIMAL TO BINARY

Write the decimal number on the right-hand side, divide by two and write down the result, placing the remainder (0 or 1) underneath this number. Divide the number obtained in the top line by 2 and carry the remainder (0 or 1) down to make a next step to the left. Repeat this operation, progressing further to the left each time, until you are left with a 0 in the top line. For example, convert the decimal number 19 to binary.

$$\begin{aligned} 19/2 &= 9, \text{ remainder } 1 \\ 9/2 &= 4, \text{ remainder } 1 \\ 4/2 &= 2, \text{ remainder } 0 \\ 2/2 &= 1, \text{ remainder } 0 \\ 1/2 &= 0, \text{ remainder } 1 \end{aligned}$$

Written as described above, we have:

decimal numbers:	0	1	2	4	9	19
remainders:	1	0	0	1	1	

and the remainders put together gives us the number 19 converted to binary, 10011.

CONVERTING BINARY TO DECIMAL

Write down progressively from *right to left* as many powers of 2 as there are digits in the binary number. Write the binary number underneath. Determine the powers of 2 in each column where a 1 appears under the heading and then *add* all these up.

Example

Binary number 10101, which has 5 digits, so write down five stages of powers of 2 starting with 2^0 and reading from right to left.

Powers of two	2^4	2^3	2^2	2^1	2^0
Write down binary number	1	0	1	0	1
Convert to decimal	16	0	4	0	1
Add	16	+ 4	+ 1	= 21	

LOGIC

Logic systems also work on the binary number process, commonly based on the difference between two *dc* voltage levels. If the more positive voltage signifies 1, then the system employs *positive* logic. If the more negative voltage signifies 1, then the system employs *negative* logic. It should be noted that in both cases, although the lower or higher voltage respectively signifies 0, this is not necessarily a *zero* voltage level, so the actual voltage values have no real significance.

There is another system, known as *pulse-logic,* where a "bit" is recognized by the presence or absence of a pulse (positive pulse in the case of a positive-logic system and negative pulse in the case of a negative-logic system).

GATES

Logic functions are performed by logic *gates*. The three basic logic functions are OR, AND and NOT. All are designed to accept two or more *input* signals and have a single *output* lead. The presence of a signal is signalled by 1 and the absence of a signal by 0.

The four possible states of an OR gate with two inputs (A and B) are shown in Fig. 10-1. There is an *output* signal whenever there is an input signal applied to input A *OR* input B (and also with input at A and B simultaneously). This applies regardless of the actual number of inputs the gate is designed to accept. The behavior of an OR gate (again written for only two inputs) is expressed by the following *truth table:*

A	B	output(Y)
0	0	0
0	1	1
1	0	1
1	1	1

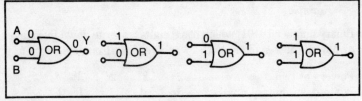

Fig. 10-1. The four states of an OR gate.

It can also be expressed in terms of Boolean algebra, calling the output Y

$$Y = A + B + \ldots + N$$
where N is the number of gates

The important thing to remember is that in Boolean algebra the sign + does not mean "plus" but OR.

The AND gate again has two or more inputs and one output, but this time the output is 1 only if *all* the inputs are also 1. The truth table in this case is quite different—Fig. 10-2. The corresponding equation of an AND gate is:

$$Y = A \bullet B \ldots N$$
$$\text{or } Y = A \times B \ldots \times N$$

This time the • or × sign does not mean "multiplied by" as in conventional arithmetic, but AND.

The NOT gate has a single input and a single output—Fig. 10-3, with output always opposite to the input, i.e., if $A = 1$, $Y = 0$ and if $A = 0$, $Y = 1$. In other words it inverts the sense of the output with respect to the input and is thus commonly called an *inverter*.

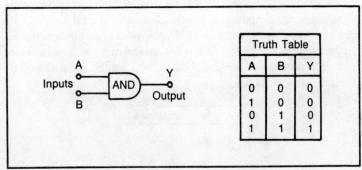

Fig. 10-2. An AND gate and corresponding truth table.

120

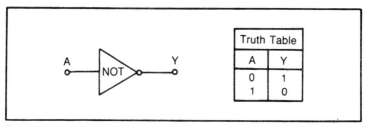

Fig. 10-3. A NOT gate and corresponding truth table.

Its Boolean equation is:

$$Y = \overline{A}$$
(Y equals NOT A)

Inverting the output of an AND gate gives us a NAND (Not AND) gate. A NAND gate is illustrated in Fig. 10-4. It is just the opposite of an AND gate. The output of a NAND gate is 0 if, and only if, both of the inputs are 1's.

Similarly, inverting the output of an OR gate results in a NOR gate, as shown in Fig. 10-5.

Another variation on the OR gate is the XOR (eXclusive OR) gate, which is illustrated in Fig. 10.6. The output is a 1 when *only one* of the inputs is a 1. This gate could also be considered a logical difference detector. If the two inputs are equal, the output is 0. If the inputs are at different logic levels, the output will be a 1.

Diode-logic (DL) circuits for an OR gate and an AND gate are shown in Fig. 10-7. Both are shown for negative logic and are identical except for the polarity of the diodes. In fact, a positive-logic DL or OR gate becomes a negative-logic AND gate; and a positive-logic AND gate a negative-logic OR gate.

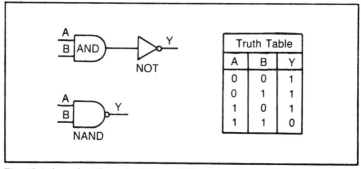

Fig. 10-4. Inverting the output of an AND gate creates a NAND gate.

121

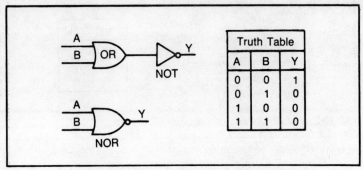

Fig. 10-5. Inverting the output of an OR gate creates a NOR gate.

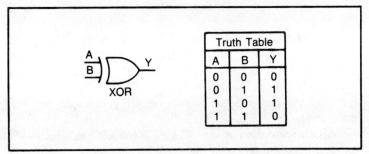

Fig. 10-6. A variation on the basic OR gate is the XOR (eXclusive OR) gate.

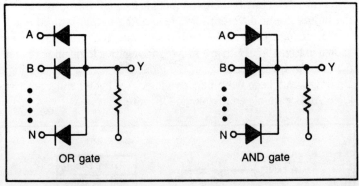

Fig. 10-7. A Diode Logic (DL) negative logic OR circuit (*left*) and a DL negative logic AND gate (*right*).

The simple NOT gate or inverter shown in Fig. 10-8 is based on a transistor logic—an NPN transistor for positive-logic and a PNP transistor for negative-logic. The capacitor across the input resistance is added to improve the transient response.

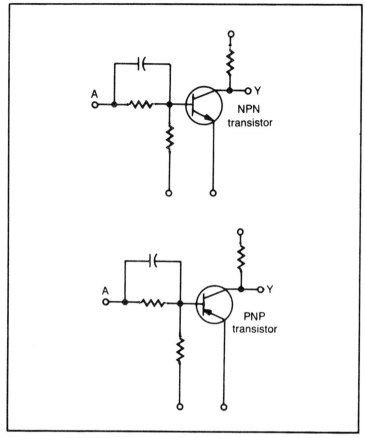

Fig. 10-8. Transistor Logic (TL) positive logic inverter circuit (*top*) and a TL negative logic NOT circuit (*bottom*).

PRACTICAL GATES

Most logic gates are produced in the form of integrated circuits, from which various "family" names are derived. NAND and NOR gates, for example, are a combination of AND or OR gates, respectively, with a NOT gate inverter. From the basic circuits just described, such functions can be performed by diode-transistor logic or DTL gates.

Faster and better performance can be realized with transistor-transistor-logic gates (TTL). During the early 1970's DTL and TTL represented the bulk of the IC digital productions, but since then various other IC families have appeared, each offering specific advantages and more functions for particular applications. These are:

RTL (resistor-transistor logic) which can be made very small—even by microelectronic standards—and is capable of performing a large number of functions.

DCTL (direct-coupled-transistor logic), which employs the same type of circuit as RTL but with the base resistors omitted. This gate, which can perform NOR or NAND functions, has the advantage of needing only one low voltage supply and has low-power classification.

HTL (high threshold logic) is based on diode-transistor logic similar to DTL but also incorporates a zener diode to stabilize the circuit and provide high immunity to "noise." It is usually chosen for applications where this feature is important.

MOS (metal oxide semiconductor logic), based entirely on field effect transistors (FETs) to the complete exclusion of diodes, resistors and capacitors, yielding NAND and NOR gates.

CMOS (complementary metal-oxide-semiconductor logic) using complementary enhancement devices on the same IC chip, reducing the power dissipation to very low levels. The basic CMOS circuit is a NOT gate (inverter), but more complicated NAND and NOR gates and also flip-flops can be formed from combinations of smaller circuits (again in a single chip).

ECL (emitter-coupled logic) also known as *CML* (current-mode logic). This family is based on a differential amplifier which is basically an analog device. Nevertheless it has important application in digital logic and is the fastest of all the logic families with delay times as low as 1 nanosecond per gate.

GATE DEMONSTRATION CIRCUITS

To give you a better understanding of how digital gates work, we will present several demonstration circuits built around the CD4011 quad NAND gate. Any digital gate can be constructed from NAND gates.

In Fig. 10-9 we have the basic NAND circuit. The LED will be lit (logic 1) if one or both inputs (A or B) are grounded (logic 0). If both of the switches is moved to the + V line (logic 1), the LED will be dark (logic 0).

By shorting the two inputs together into a single input line, as shown in Fig. 10-10 we have a simple inverter demonstrator. If the input is logic 1 (V +), the output will be logic 0 (LED dark). If the input is logic 0 (ground), then the output will be logic 1 (LED lit).

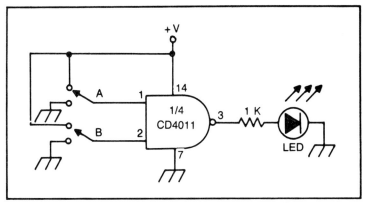

Fig. 10-9. This simple circuit demonstrates the operation of a NAND gate.

Inverting the output of a NAND gate produces an AND gate. This can be done with two NAND gate stages, as illustrated in Fig. 10-11.

On the other hand, inverting the inputs of a NAND gate simulates an OR gate. A demonstration circuit for this is shown in Fig. 10-12.

Simply adding a fourth stage (as an inverter) creates a NOR gate, as illustrated in Fig. 10-13.

A number of non-standard gating schemes can also be created. For example, the circuit shown in Fig. 10-14 is a combined AND/OR gate. The output is a logic 1 if A and B are 1's or C and D are 1's. If all four inputs are 1's, the output will also be a 1.

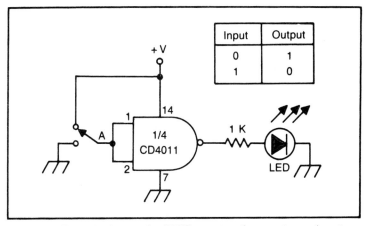

Input	Output
0	1
1	0

Fig. 10-10. Tying the inputs of a NAND gate together creates an inverter.

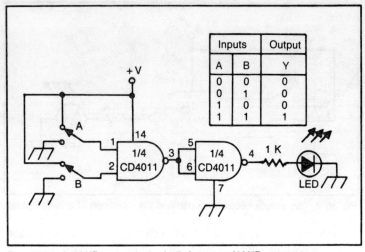

Inputs		Output
A	B	Y
0	0	0
0	1	0
1	0	0
1	1	1

Fig. 10-11. An AND gate can be built from two NAND gate stages.

Digital gates can be used for more than simple logic switching applications. The circuit in Fig. 10-15 is a simple low frequency square wave oscillator. When the input is a logic 1 (connected to V +), the circuit will oscillate. The LED will blink on and off once

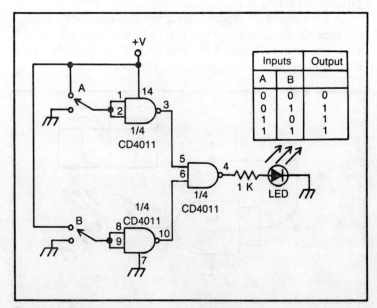

Inputs		Output
A	B	
0	0	0
0	1	1
1	0	1
1	1	1

Fig. 10-12. This circuit demonstrates how an OR gate can be created from three NAND gates.

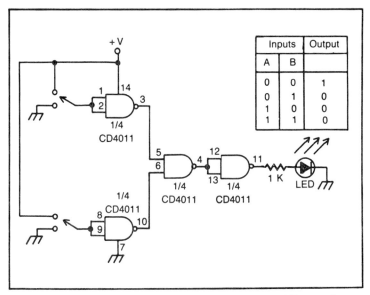

Inputs		Output
A	B	
0	0	1
0	1	0
1	0	0
1	1	0

Fig. 10-13. Adding an inverter stage to the OR gate circuit of Fig. 10-12 turns it into a NOR gate.

or twice a second. A logic 0 at the input (grounded) disables the oscillator.

Try different capacitor values to create other frequencies. If the frequency is too high, the eye will not be able to distinguish between the separate blinks. The LED will appear to stay continuously lit when the oscillator is enabled.

Try routing the output to a small speaker when using a smaller capacitor. (A 0.1 μF capacitor would be a good choice.) You will hear a tone from the speaker when the oscillator is enabled.

FLIP-FLOPS

A flip-flop is a bistable circuit and another important element in digital logic. Since it is capable of storing *one* bit of information it is functionally a *1-bit memory unit*. Because this information is locked or "latched" in place, a flip-flop is also known as a *latch*. A combination of n flip-flops can thus store an *n-bit word*, such a unit being referred to as a *register*.

A basic flip-flop circuit is formed by cross-coupling two NOT gates, the output of each gate being connected back to the input of the other gate. The NOT gates can be created from NAND gates as described earlier, and the final circuit will look like Fig. 10-16.

127

However, to be able to preset or clear the state of the flip-flop, two NAND gates are necessary, each preceded by a NOT gate, or a NAND gate with its inputs joined. See Fig. 10-17.

When the flip-flop is used in a pulsed or clocked system the preceding gates are known as the *steering* gates with the cross-coupled two-input gates forming the *latch*. This particular config-

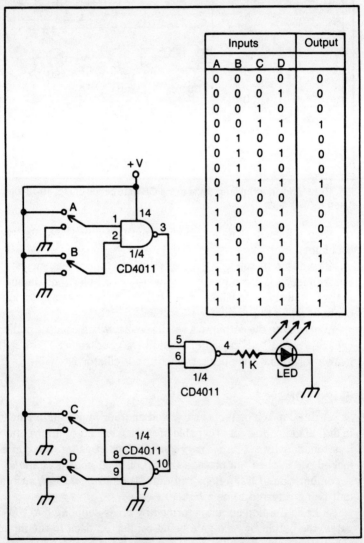

Fig. 10-14. This circuit demonstrates how basic gates can be combined into non-standard gating arrangements.

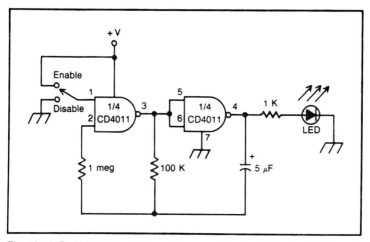

Fig. 10-15. Digital gates can be used for more than just simple switching circuits. This is a gated digital square wave oscillator.

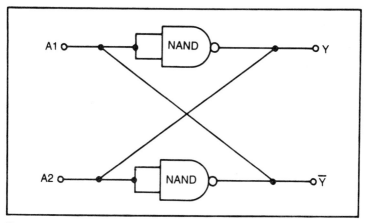

Fig. 10-16. A 1 bit memory or latch circuit is obtained by cross-coupling two NOT gates, or two NAND gates with their inputs shorted.

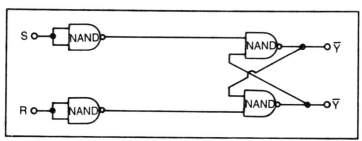

Fig. 10-17. Flip-flop circuit with preset using four NOT gates.

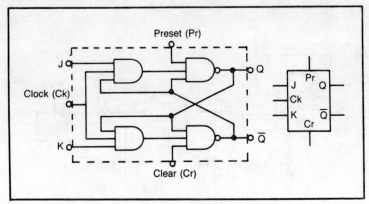

Fig. 10-18. J-K flip-flop circuit with corresponding symbol.

uration is also known as a S-R or R-S flip-flop. Two other variations of the flip-flop are also produced as integrated circuits:

J-K flip-flop—which is an S-R flip-flop preceded by two AND gates. This configuration removes any ambiguity in the truth table. It can be used as a T-type flip-flop by connecting the J and K inputs together (*see* Fig. 10-18 for connections).

D-type flip-flop—which is a J-K flip-flop modified by the addition of an inverter (*see* Fig. 10-19). It functions as a 1-bit delay device.

FLIP-FLOP DEMONSTRATION CIRCUITS

One of the most common applications for a flip-flop is frequency division. The frequency at the output of a flip-flop stage will be one half the frequency of a square wave input signal.

Figure 10-20 shows a simple demonstration circuit for this type of application. It consists of two stages. The first stage (IC1 and its associated components) is a simple 555 astable multivibrator (see

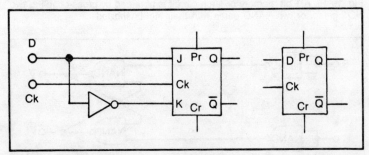

Fig. 10-19. A D-type flip-flop circuit is provided by a J-K flip-flop allied with an inverter.

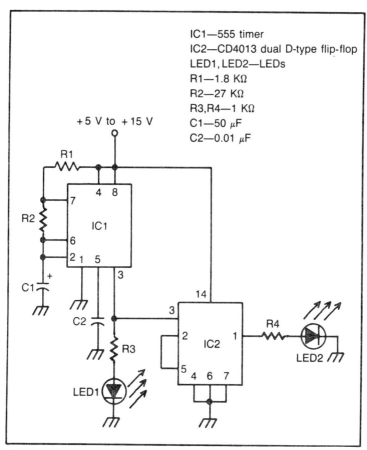

Fig. 10-20. This circuit demonstrates how a flip-flop can be used for frequency division.

Chapter 7). With the component values listed, it will produce a near square wave with a frequency of about 1 Hz. The second stage (IC2) is one half a dual D type flip-flop IC (CD4013). The frequency is divided by two in this stage.

LED1 will blink on and off approximately once a second, while LED2 (the output) will blink once every other time LED1 (the input) blinks.

Any number of flip-flop stages can be strung together. By looking at each stage output, a binary counter can be created. A simple modulo-8 counter circuit is shown in Fig. 10-21. This circuit will count from 0 (0000) to 8 (1000), then cycle back to 0 and start over. That is:

131

```
0000
0001
0010
0011
0100
0101
0110
0111
1000
0000
0001
0010
```

and so forth.

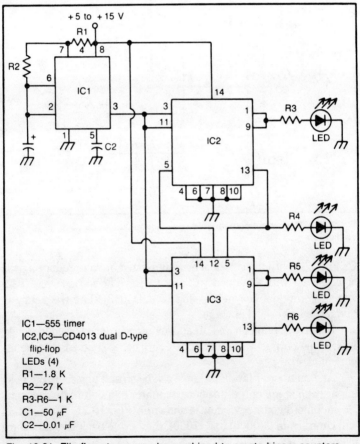

Fig. 10-21. Flip-flop stages can be combined to create binary counters.

A variation on the basic flip-flop counter circuit is shown in Fig. 10-22. Here only one LED will be lit (logic 1) at any given moment. The circuit will step through the four outputs repeatedly, activating one at a time. This type of circuit is sometimes called a 1-of-4 sequencer. It can be extended to include as many output stages as desired.

FAN-IN AND FAN-OUT

The terms *fan-in* and *fan-out* are used with IC logic devices. Fan-in refers to the number of separate inputs to a logic gate. Fan-out is the number of circuit loads the output can accommodate, or in other words the number of separate outputs provided. Fan-out is commonly 10, meaning that the output of the gate can be connected to 10 standard inputs on matching gates. Each separate input represents a load, the higher the number of separate loads the higher the current output of the device providing fan-out needs to be in order to provide the *standard load* on each input, i.e., passing enough current to drop each input voltage to the design figure.

It is possible to increase fan-out by replacing diode(s) with transistor(s) in the device concerned, so 10 is by no means a maximum number.

ROM

ROM stands for Read-Only Memory, a system capable of converting one code into another. The best known application is to convert the reading of a digital instrument such as an electronic calculator into a numerical read-out via an LED (light emitting diode) display. The advantage of a ROM is that it is programmable and thus adaptable to different read-out systems. It does not follow, however, that it uses the minimum number of components to match a particular application. Special IC chips designed for a specific application may be more economic in this respect, but not necessarily in cost, unless there is a very large demand for that particular IC. The calculator market is a case in point where a special chip can offer advantages over a ROM.

RAM

RAM stands for Random-Access Memory and is basically a collection of flip-flops or similar devices capable of memorizing information in binary form. Information can be written-in or read out in a random manner.

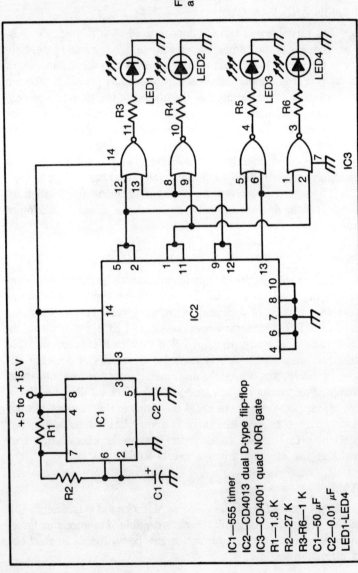

Fig. 10-22. This circuit is a 1-of-4 sequencer.

IC1—555 timer
IC2—CD4013 dual D-type flip-flop
IC3—CD4001 quad NOR gate
R1—1.8 K
R2—27 K
R3-R6—1 K
C1—50 µF
C2—0.01 µF
LED1-LED4

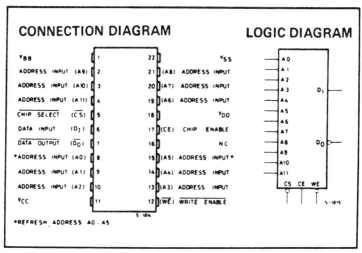

Fig. 10-23. Example of a Random Access Memory integrated circuit with connection diagram.

THE SHAPE OF DIGITAL ICs

In physical appearance, most digital ICs look like any other dual in-line (or sometimes quad in-line) IC package, or ceramic flat packages. They are not readily identified as digital ICs, therefore, (except by type number) although their function is quite specific. The more complicated digital ICs may, however, have considerably more pins than usual. It is also common practice to give pin diagrams which not only define the pin positions but also their specific function (Fig. 10-23).

Chapter 11

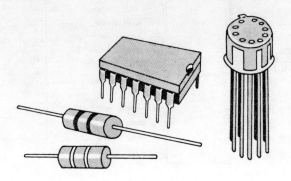

Electronic Organs

One of the major problems in the design of electronic organs is the large number of mechanical contacts called for using conventional (discrete component) circuitry. With two manuals of four octaves each, for example, 98 mechanical contacts are needed. This not only complicates construction but could also be a source of trouble in operation. There is often the limitation that each key is only able to play one note. It is desirable for electronic organs to be able to play more than one octave-related note per key, increasing the number of mechanical contacts required by that factor, e.g., 5 × 98 = 490 contacts for the example quoted to be able to play five octave-related notes per key.

A number of integrated circuits have been developed, usually based on digital logic, to overcome such limitations. Many also provide additional features which may be desirable. An example is the (Mullard) TDA1008 which consists of a matrix of gate circuits with eight divide-by-two gates in each circuit. It is a 16-lead dual-in-line plastic package (SOT-38).

One drive input only is required for delivering nine octave-related notes and, by actuating a key input, five successive signals out of the nine can be selected and transferred to the output. Five key inputs are available, each selecting a different combination. Other features which are available are "sustain" and "percussion" of the output signals; and also "decay" of modulations.

Further simplification of an electronic organ circuit can also be provided by using a top octave synthesizer (TOS) instead of a series of master oscillators to derive the twelve top octave frequencies required for a "full" organ. A TOS must be associated with a *master oscillator* capable of generating a suitable "least common multiple" frequency, with the TOS following it, then providing the twelve highest notes. Used with a suitable gating matrix, further sub-multiples of these notes are obtained, e.g., in the case of the TDA1008 the following output frequencies are available from the five keys, where f is the actual input frequency:

	key 1	key 2	key 3	key 4	key 5
output 1	f	f/2	f/4	f/8	f/16
output 2	f/2	f/4	f/8	f/16	f/32
output 3	f/4	f/8	f/16	f/32	f/64
output 4	f/8	f/16	f/32	f/64	f/128
output 5	f/16	f/32	f/64	f/128	f/256

This, in effect gives nine different notes available from each of twelve available input frequencies from the TOS, or 96 different notes. Further, operating two or more keys simultaneously will give the sum signal of these frequencies.

MASTER OSCILLATOR

A suitable frequency for the master oscillator is about 4.5 MHz. A variety of circuits can be used providing they have suitable stability and the necessary amplitude and slew rate for driving the TOS properly. If the master oscillator is a sine wave generator, then it will be necessary to follow this with a Schmitt trigger to obtain the required slew rate. This is not necessary with a square-wave generator and a very simple circuit of this latter type based on the NAND gates contained in the CD4011 integrated circuit is shown in Fig. 11-1. This requires a stabilized 12-volt supply, as does the TDA1008, so the same supply can be used for both the master oscillator and TDA1008.

The master oscillator output connects to the Top Octave Synthesizer, the tone outputs of which form the input to the TDA1008. They can be directly connected since the input signal pin of the TDA1008 has an impedance of at least 28 KΩ.

GATE MATRIX

Connections to the TDA1008 integrated circuit are shown in

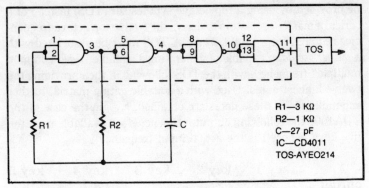

R1—3 KΩ
R2—1 KΩ
C—27 pF
IC—CD4011
TOS-AYEO214

Fig. 11-1. Master (square-wave) oscillator circuit to feed top octave Synthesizer.

Fig. 11-2. The different levels of supply voltage required are 6 volts, 9 volts and 12 volts, as shown. The five keys can be directly connected, although current-limiting resistors can be used in each key line if necessary.

Five different output frequencies are available at each output Q1, Q2, Q3, Q4, Q5, depending on which key is activated (*see* table above). To avoid sub-harmonics being generated it is advisable to connect any not-required Q outputs to the +6 volt supply line.

SUSTAIN

To actuate sustain and percussion effects, a time-delay circuit can be added associated with each key, as shown in Fig. 11-3. This circuit will sustain the tone(s) for a period after release of the key, but with the resistor also providing a certain delay time. The addition of a series resistor (RS) will delay the build-up of notes, depending on the RC time constant of this resistor and the associated capacitor in the circuit. Component values given are selected for good tonal response, but this is also a matter of personal preference and so some adjustment of values may be preferred. It is also possible to shorten the decay time of the sustain by adjusting the voltage applied to pin 7. A circuit for doing this is shown in Fig. 11-4.

PERCUSSION

If percussion is required this can be arranged by connecting a capacitor to pin 8 to discharge during keying, associated with a series resistor to give a suitable time constant. Using a 0.47 F capacitor, a suitable series resistor value can be found by experiment.

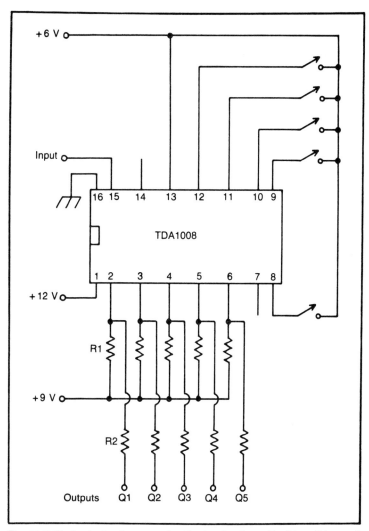

Fig. 11-2. Basic electronic organ circuit using five keys. Resistors R1 are all 1 KΩ. Resistors R2 are all 100 KΩ. Q1, Q2, Q3, Q4 and Q5 are the tone outputs to feed an audio amplifier circuit with loudspeaker.

The decay time is also adjustable via the circuit shown in Fig. 11-4.

To retain sustain as well, the circuit shown in Fig. 11-5 should be used. If sustain is wanted, switch S1 is closed and switch S2 opened. C1 then remains charged to sustain the note as long as a key is held down. Once the key is released the note will decay at the rate established by the decay circuit connected to pin 7. To operate percussion, switch S1 is open and switch S2 closed.

TOP OCTAVE GENERATOR

A readily available, easy-to-use top octave generator in IC form is the MK50240. A high speed clock signal is fed to the input, and puts out twelve equally tempered tones (one full octave) plus one extra note. The pitch can be varied by changing the clock frequency. One nice feature of any circuit built around the MK50240 is that any such instrument will always be in tune with itself.

The basic organ circuit using this chip is shown in Fig. 11-6. The range can easily be extended with flip-flop stages, as shown

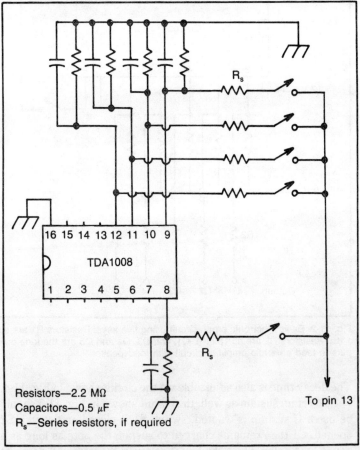

Resistors—2.2 MΩ
Capacitors—0.5 μF
Rs—Series resistors, if required

To pin 13

Fig. 11-3. "Sustain" added to the circuit of Fig. 12-2. Other components are connected as before.

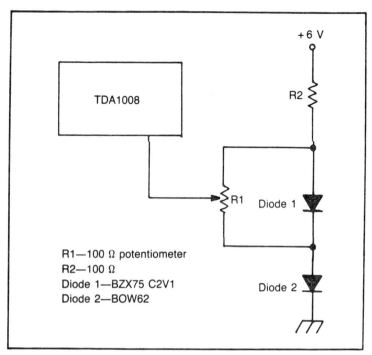

Fig. 11-4. Adjustable voltage to pin 7 for decay control.

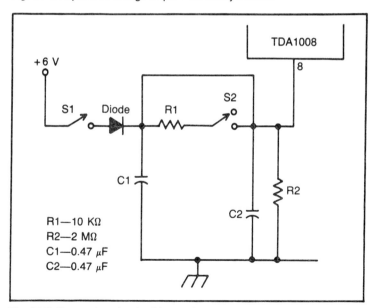

Fig. 11-5. Percussion circuit with sustain, connecting to pin 8.

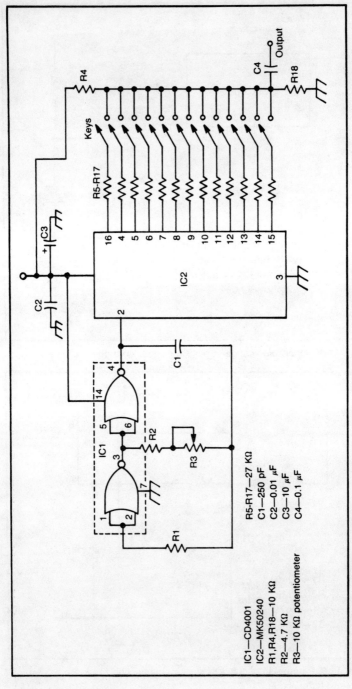

IC1—CD4001
IC2—MK50240
R1, R4, R18—10 KΩ
R2—4.7 KΩ
R3—10 KΩ potentiometer

R5-R17—27 KΩ
C1—250 pF
C2—0.01 μF
C3—10 μF
C4—0.1 μF

Fig. 11-6. A simple organ can easily be built around the MK50240 top octave generator IC.

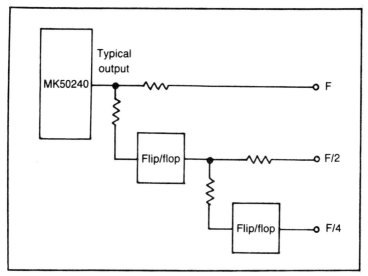

Fig. 11-7. The range of the organ circuit shown in Fig. 11-6 can be extended with flip-flop frequency dividers.

in Fig. 11-7. Each flip-flop divides the signal by two, or drops it exactly one octave.

More than a single note can be produced at a time. The MK50240 is fully polyphonic. It is capable of chords. Fig. 11-8 shows how chords can be hard-wired to allow for one switch operations.

The MK50240 can also be used as a random voltage source. This is done by lowering the clock frequency to a few hundred Hz, or less. A random voltage generator circuit is shown in Fig. 11-9.

SOUND EFFECTS CIRCUITS

Simple electronic organs, like the ones we have described so far, generate square waves (or other rectangle waves). This gives a pleasing, musical tone, but it is undeniably limited. Some tonal variety can be achieved with various filtering circuits. But in some applications, you may want to create other types of sounds.

A number of sound effects ICs have been developed in the last few years. These devices are essentially a complete (albeit simple) electronic sound synthesizer in a single chip. The SN94281 is a typical complex sound generator IC. It is shown in Fig. 11-10. A block diagram of its internal circuitry is shown in Fig. 11-11. The sub-circuits can be connected in various ways with a handful of exter-

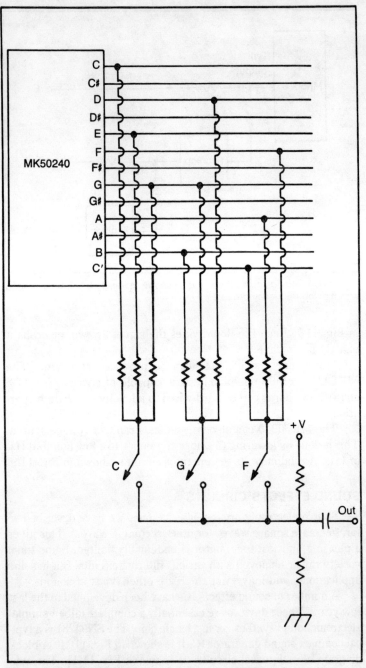

Fig. 11-8. The MK50240 can be hard-wired for single touch chords.

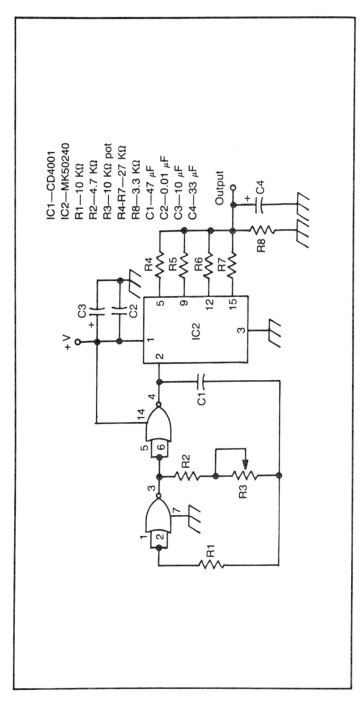

IC1—CD4001
IC2—MK50240
R1—10 KΩ
R2—4.7 KΩ
R3—10 KΩ pot
R4-R7—27 KΩ
R8—3.3 KΩ
C1—47 μF
C2—0.01 μF
C3—10 μF
C4—33 μF

Fig. 11-9. The MK50240 can also be used as a random voltage source.

145

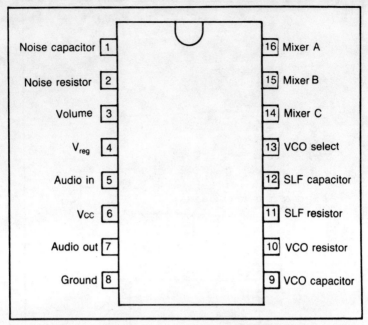

Fig. 11-10. The SN94281 is used to generate many different sound effects.

nal resistors and capacitors to produce literally thousands of different sounds. Some sounds will be quite musical, and others will be unquestionably non-musical.

A simple circuit built around the SN94281 is shown in Fig. 11-12. With the following component values, the sounds produced will be like a space laser gun out of a science fiction movie;

$$
\begin{array}{rcl}
C1 & = & 10 \ \mu F \\
R1 & = & 1K \\
R2 & = & 1.5K \\
C2 & = & 0.1 \ \mu F
\end{array}
$$

Other very different effects can be achieved with the same circuit, simply by changing the component values. Try these components;

$$
\begin{array}{rcl}
C1 & = & 0.1 \ \mu F \\
R1 & = & 1 \ Meg \\
R2 & = & 470K \\
C2 & = & 0.001 \ \mu F
\end{array}
$$

146

or;

$$C1 = 0.1 \ \mu F$$
$$R1 = 100K$$
$$R2 = 220K$$
$$C2 = 0.05 \ \mu F$$

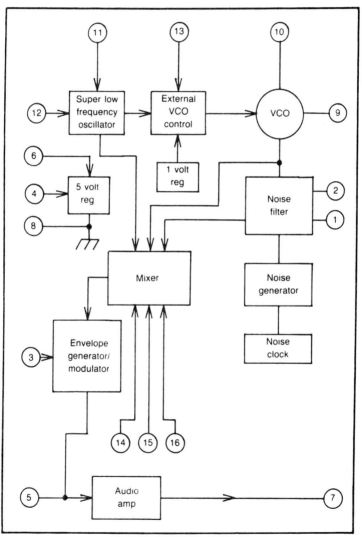

Fig. 11-11. The SN94281 is a complete sound synthesizer system in a single IC chip.

147

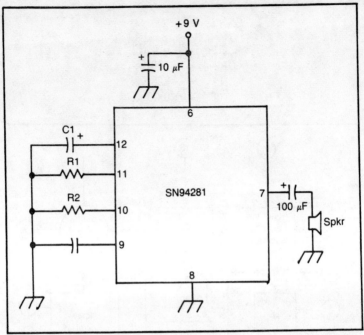

Fig. 11-12. This circuit can be used to generate many different sound effects by changing the component values. Some examples are described in the text.

or almost anything else. Some of the effects are difficult to survive, but they are fascinating to experiment with.

Chapter 12

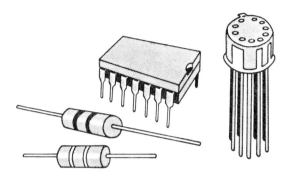

Miscellaneous Circuits

This chapter covers many IC circuits that do not fall into any of the previous categories. These projects range from LED displays for radio tuning, to intercoms, to infrared transmitters and receivers.

After this final chapter of projects, there is a chapter on construction methods which will help you build all of these projects with good, solid techniques that will make your projects work better, and will make your building more enjoyable.

HI-FI TONE CONTROLS

Tone controls fitted to domestic radios and equivalent circuits are seldom of high quality. This does not usually matter for AM reception (which can never be Hi-Fi); but can degrade the performance on FM reception. Similar remarks apply to the tone controls fitted to lower priced record players and tape recorders.

High quality tone controls generally demand quite complex circuits. ICs enable the number of discrete components required to be substantially reduced and, at the same time, offer other advantages such as a high input impedance which matches a typical high impedance source. Tone control can also be combined with audio amplification in IC circuits.

Figure 12-1 shows a complete circuit based around a TCA8305 integrated circuit incorporating a feedback network which attenu-

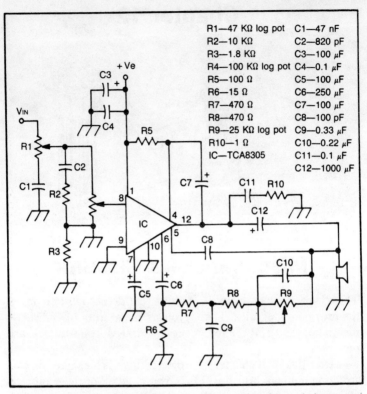

R1—47 KΩ log pot C1—47 nF
R2—10 KΩ   C2—820 pF
R3—1.8 KΩ   C3—100 μF
R4—100 KΩ log pot C4—0.1 μF
R5—100 Ω   C5—100 μF
R6—15 Ω   C6—250 μF
R7—470 Ω   C7—100 μF
R8—470 Ω   C8—100 pF
R9—25 KΩ log pot C9—0.33 μF
R10—1 Ω   C10—0.22 μF
IC—TCA8305   C11—0.1 μF
                   C12—1000 μF

Fig. 12-1. Hi-Fi tone control circuit suitable for receivers, record players and tape recorders and characterized by a high input impedance. Potentiometer R1 is the treble control. Potentiometer R9 is the bass control. Potentiometer R4 is the volume control.

ates the low frequencies and boosts the high frequencies. At the same time high frequencies can be attenuated by the treble control potentiometer at the input. The volume control, also on the input side, provides "loudness control" at both high and low frequencies to compensate for the loss of sensitivity of the human ear to such frequencies (i.e., both high and low frequencies tend to sound "less loud" to the ear).

A simpler circuit, using the same IC, is shown in Fig. 12-2. This has a single tone control potentiometer. The circuit provides flat response at middle frequencies (i.e., around 1 kHz), with marked boost and cut of up to ± 10 decibels at 110 Hz and 10 kHz respectively in the extreme position of the potentiometer.

A (Baxandall) Hi-Fi tone control circuit associated with another type of op-amp is shown in Fig. 12-3. The IC in this case is the

CA3140 BiMOS op-amp. The tone control circuit is conventional and only a few additional discrete components are required to complete the amplifier circuit around the IC. This circuit is capable of ± 15 decibels bass and treble boost and cut at 100 Hz and 10 kHz respectively.

An alternative circuit using the same IC and giving a similar performance is shown in Fig. 12-4. Both of these circuits require a supply voltage of 30-32 volts. Figure 12-5 shows the same circuit modified for dual supplies.

LED DISPLAY BRIGHTNESS CONTROL

How well an LED shows up is dependent on the ambient light

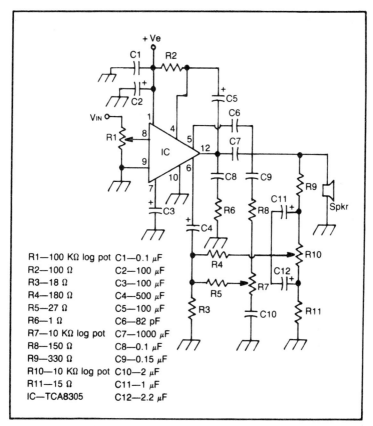

R1—100 KΩ log pot   C1—0.1 μF
R2—100 Ω   C2—100 μF
R3—18 Ω   C3—100 μF
R4—180 Ω   C4—500 μF
R5—27 Ω   C5—100 μF
R6—1 Ω   C6—82 pF
R7—10 KΩ log pot   C7—1000 μF
R8—150 Ω   C8—0.1 μF
R9—330 Ω   C9—0.15 μF
R10—10 KΩ log pot   C10—2 μF
R11—15 Ω   C11—1 μF
IC—TCA8305   C12—2.2 μF

Fig. 12-2. Alternative Hi-Fi tone control circuit with separate high and low frequency feedback. Potentiometer R1 is the volume control. Potentiometer R7 is the treble control and potentiometer R10 the bass control.

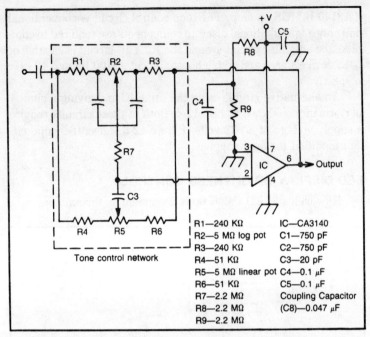

Fig. 12-3. Simple Hi-Fi tone control circuit. Component values are determined for a supply voltage of 32 volts. Potentiometer R2 is the bass control. Potentiometer R5 is the treble control. Components within the dashed outline comprise the tone control network.

falling on it. In dim light the display is usually quite bright. In direct sunlight it may be difficult to see at all. The circuit shown in Fig. 12-6 provides an automatic brightness control of a (single) LED by using a silicon photodiode to sense the amount of ambient light and feed a proportional signal to the TCA315 op-amp integrated circuit. As the intensity of light increases the output current from the op-amp increases in proportion, and vice versa, thus automatically compensating the brightness of the LED for artificial light. The brighter the ambient light, the brighter the LED glows, and vice versa.

The potentiometer (R6) is used for setting up the circuit initially. With a 2.5 volt supply, and with the photodiode in complete darkness, R6 should be adjusted to give a current reading of about 100 μA (0.1 milliamps), using a meter in one battery lead to check. With this adjustment, and the type of photodiode specified, the LED will then receive an impressed current of 5 mA per 1000 lux illumination of the photodiode.

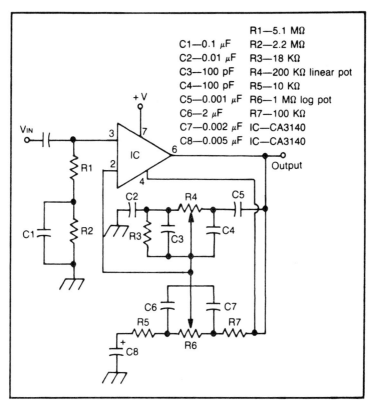

Fig. 12-4. Another Hi-Fi tone control circuit. Potentiometer R4 is the treble control. Potentiometer R6 is the bass control. Supply voltage is 30 volts.

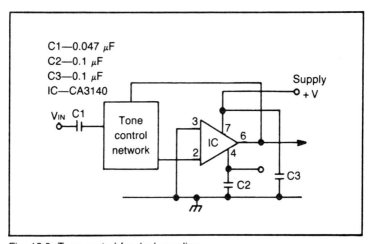

Fig. 12-5. Tone control for dual supplies.

LED RADIO TUNING SCALE

This simple circuit displays the tuned frequency of a radio in terms of spots of light instead of (or in addition to) the usual pointer moving over a scale. An array of 16 LEDs should be sufficient to indicate station positions with suitable accuracy over a typical medium frequency waveband (i.e., 520 kHz to 1600 kHz). The display is driven by a Siemens UAA170 integrated circuit. A phototransistor is also used to match the brightness of the display automatically to ambient light intensity, i.e., dimming the display in dull light and brightening the display to make it clearly visible in sunlight.

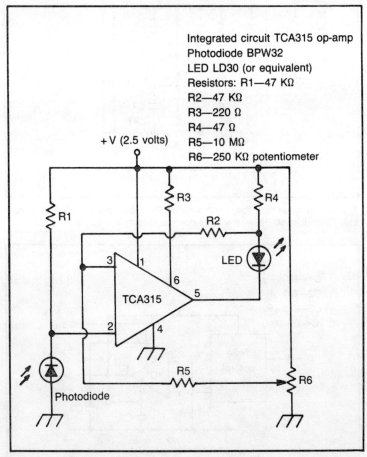

Integrated circuit TCA315 op-amp
Photodiode BPW32
LED LD30 (or equivalent)
Resistors: R1—47 KΩ
R2—47 KΩ
R3—220 Ω
R4—47 Ω
R5—10 MΩ
R6—250 KΩ potentiometer

+ V (2.5 volts)

Fig. 12-6. Circuit for automatic control of brightness of an LED using a photodiode to sense the level of illumination.

The complete circuit is shown in Fig. 12-7. The UAA170 is controlled via the voltage divider formed by R1 and R2 supplying the tuning voltage for the AM tuning diode incorporated in the IC. Since this diode has non-linear characteristics, stations on the left (lower frequency) end of the tuning scale will be more closely concentrated, consistent with station spacing on this broadcast band.

The circuit will work on most normal transistor radio supply voltages (i.e., V_s = 10 to 18 volts), and with an input voltage for frequency indication of V_s = 1.2 to 27 volts using two (Siemens) LD468 LED-arrays. Voltage at the divider point between R1 and R2 should be between 0.06 and 1.16 volts and can be adjusted by R1 if necessary. The actual brightness of the display is automatically controlled by the phototransistor BP101/1, and is also adjustable via the 1 KΩ potentiometer.

CAR THIEF ALARM

This is another circuit originated by Siemens and based around their TDB0556A dual timer IC. The first timing circuit of this device is used as a bistable multivibrator with the circuit activated by switch S1. Output level remains at zero, set by the voltage applied to the threshold input pin 2 until one of the alarm contact switches is closed, causing C1 to discharge.

"Press-for-off" alarm switches can be fitted to the doors, bonnet and boot lid, so arranged that opening of a door or lid completes that switch contact. This will produce an output signal held for about 8 seconds, pulling in the relay after an initial delay of about 4 seconds. The horn circuit is completed by the relay contacts so the horn will sound for 8 seconds. After this the relay will drop out (shutting off the horn) until capacitor C1 charges up again. This will take about 3 seconds, when the relay will pull in once more and the horn will sound again. This varying signal of 8 seconds horn on, 3 seconds horn off, will be repeated until switch S1 is turned off (or the battery is flattened). This type of alarm signal commands more attention than a continuous sounding alarm such as can be given by straightforward on-off electrical switching.

The complete circuit is shown in Fig. 12-8 with suitable component values, wired in to appropriate points on a car electrical system.

INTERCOM

The TCA830S is a powerful, inexpensive op-amp IC which

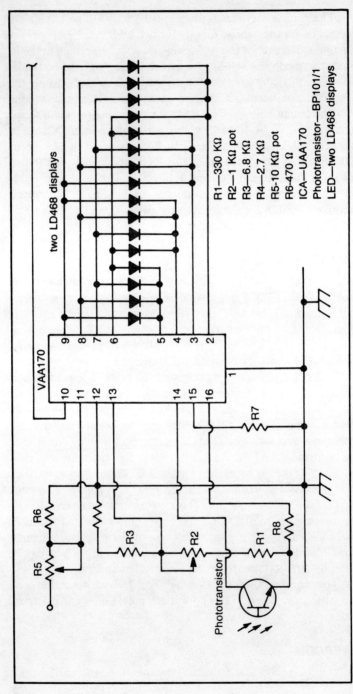

R1—330 KΩ
R2—1 KΩ pot
R3—6.8 KΩ
R4—2.7 KΩ
R5-10 KΩ pot
R6-470 Ω
ICA—UAA170
Phototransistor—BP101/1
LED—two LD468 displays

two LD468 displays

VAA170

Phototransistor

Fig. 12-7. Sixteen LED display to replace or augment the usual pointer and scale indication of tuned frequency on an AM radio receiver.

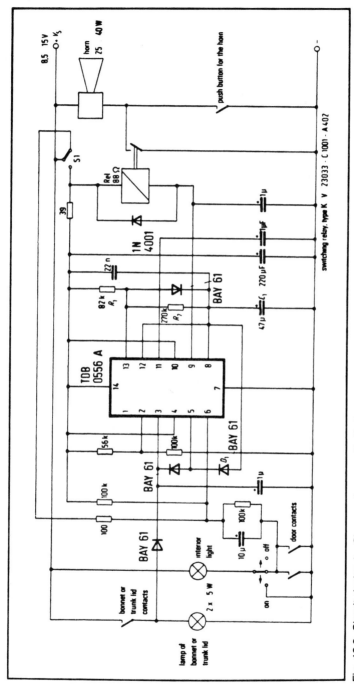

Fig. 12-8. Circuit design by Siemens for a car theft alarm.

makes it a particularly attractive choice for intercoms since the circuit can be built with a minimum number of components. Many other op-amps do not produce the power required for loudspeaker operation without the addition of a further stage of transistor amplification. The basic circuit is contained at the "main" station while the "distant" station merely comprises a loudspeaker and a "calling" switch. The two stations are connected by a 3-wire flex.

The circuit is shown in Fig. 12-9. The TCA830S requires a heat sink and is fitted with tabs. A printed circuit is recommended, incorporating two 1 in. (25 mm) squares of copper to which the IC tabs can be soldered for the heat sink. Component positioning is not critical since the circuit handles only audio frequencies.

The transformer (T) has a 50:1 turns ratio and is used as a step-down transformer between the IC and speaker(s)—also working as a step-up transformer between speaker(s) and IC for working in the reverse mode. In other words the transformer coil with the larger number of turns is connected to pin 8 on the IC. Instead of purchasing this transformer ready-made it can be wound on a stack of standard transformer core laminates 0.35 mm thick, giving a core

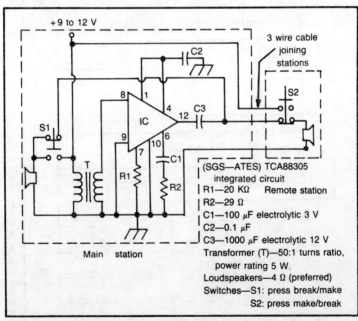

Fig. 12-9. Intercom circuit using the TCA830S integrated circuit. This IC is powerful enough to operate fairly large loudspeakers. Component values are given in the text.

cross-section of 22.5 mm^2. Windings are 600 turns of 0.2 mm (36 s.w.g.) and 300 turns of 0.06 mm (46 s.w.g.) enamelled copper wire.

The purpose of the transformer is to enable standard 4 to 16-Ω loudspeakers to be used both as microphones and speakers. These speakers can be of any size, bearing in mind that the maximum power output of the circuit is of the order of 2 watts on a 12-volt supply. The intercom circuit will work on any battery voltage down to 6 volts, 9 or 12 volts being recommended for general operation.

ICE WARNING INDICATOR

This very simple circuit uses a thermistor as a temperature sensor together with three CA3401E op-amps and a minimum of external components. The operating point of the circuit is set by the potentiometer (R2) so that, at an ambient air temperature approaching freezing point, the light emitting diode (LED) starts to flash. As the temperature falls, the rate of flashing increases until the LED glows continuously once freezing point is reached. Accurate calibration can be carried out in the freezer compartment of a domestic refrigerator with the door open, in conjunction with a thermometer.

The complete circuit is shown in Fig. 12-10. IC1, IC2 and IC3 are separate op-amp circuits contained in the IC. Thus pins 1 and 6 are the input to IC1 and pin 5 the output of IC1; pins 11 and 12 the input to IC2 and pin 10 the output of IC2; and pins 2 and 3 the input to IC3 and pin 4 the output of IC3. Pins 8, 9 and 13 are ignored. Pin 7 connects to the earth side of the circuit; and pin 14 to battery plus side.

Layout of this circuit is not critical but all component leads should be kept as short as possible and the LED located some distance away from the integrated circuit. This circuit is powered by a 12 volt battery.

DIGITAL VOLTMETER

A digital voltmeter (known as a DVM) has several advantages over a conventional pointer-and-needle meter, for example:

- Easier reading with direct presentation of reading in digits.
- Greater accuracy and high speed of reading.
- Higher sensitivity.
- Greater resolution.

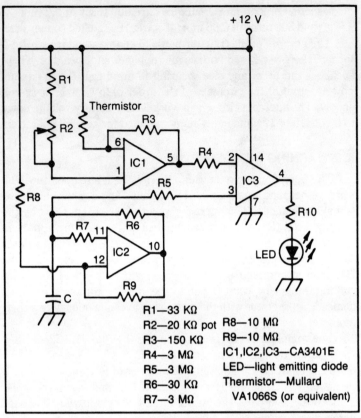

Fig. 12-10. Circuit for an ice-warning indicator. Adjustment of potentiometer R2 can set the circuit to flash the LED as air temperature approaches freezing point, with LED staying permanently alight once freezing temperature is reached.

Unfortunately, the circuitry required for a DVM is quite complicated, making it much more expensive than its simple analog counterpart in the form of a moving coil instrument. However, by using ICs the necessary circuitry for a DVM can be simplified and miniaturized and is within the scope of the amateur to build. The following design by Siemens avoids the use of expensive components and its performance is comparable with that of ready-made DVMs in the medium-price range (well over $100). It has a basic range of up to 9.9 volts with an accuracy of better than 99 percent.

The complete circuit is shown in Fig. 12-11. The input voltage is converted to a proportional frequency by the op-amp TBA221 connected as an integrating amplifier and the following monosta-

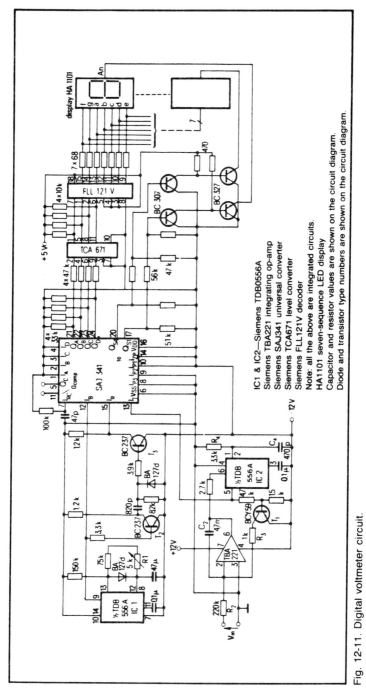

Fig. 12-11. Digital voltmeter circuit.

161

ble multivibrator TDB556A (IC2). The resulting output pulse (at pin 5 of IC2) is determined by the time constant of R4 and C4 and is of the order of 1.5 μs. This pulse turns transistor T1 "on" and "off," the multivibrator thus supplying pulses to the clock input of the counter SAJ341 with a repetition frequency proportional to the input voltage.

These pulses are counted during a measuring interval defined by the other half of the astable multivibrator TDB556A (IC1) with a duty cycle of <0.5. Its output directly controls the blocking input of the counter (SAJ341). At the beginning of each measuring interval, 5AJ341 is reset to Q_A, Q_B, Q_C, Q_D = L (corresponding to decimal 0) by a short L-pulse applied to the reset input IR. This reset pulse is produced by the measuring-interval generator, the inverting transistor T2 and the following differentiation circuit.

The display, which can be extended to four digits, operates on a time-multiplex basis using a level converter (TCA671), decoder (FLL121V) and display driving transistors BC307 and BC327.

The circuit is set up using a known input voltage (preferably between 2 and 3 volts). Potentiometer R1 is then adjusted to show the correct reading on the display. If this is not possible, then the value of resistor R2 should be changed for the next nearest value up or down, i.e., 270 or 180 kilohms as found appropriate (one value will make matters worse, the other better).

The circuit needs two separate power supplies of +5 volts at 300 milliamps and -12 volts at 200 milliamps. For accurate working of the meter both supply voltages should be regulated.

INFRARED TRANSMITTER AND RECEIVER

There are three practical possibilities for remote control signalling: radio (as in model radio control systems); ultrasonics; and light transmission. The latter is the simplest in terms of components and circuitry, especially where simple on/off command only is required. It can be extended to more channels, but at the expense of more complicated circuitry.

Using infrared light transmission it is possible to achieve a range of 100 feet (30 meters) or more quite readily in normal ambient light. Even greater range is possible if the transmitter light beam is focused by a simple lens system. Such infrared remote control systems have become highly practical with the appearance of high-efficiency LEDs with a high infrared transmission and suitable photodiodes which can be used as detectors in receivers. As with other remote control systems the basic units involved are a *transmitter* and *receiver*.

Single-Channel Infrared Transmitter

This circuit uses the Siemens LD27 improved light-emitting diode LD27 in a pulse modulated transmitter circuit involving the use of two oscillators, a sub-carrier frequency of 50 kHz modulated by a frequency of 10 Hz, the second oscillator having a duty cycle of 250:1. These circuits are based around four CMOS NAND-gates (available in a single IC). The LED is square-wave modulated by a Darlington pair of NPN transistors.

The complete transmitter circuit is shown in Fig. 12-12 and is quite straightforward. Despite drawing a peak current of 1 amp, the average current drain is only 2 mA with a 6-volt battery supply, the peak current actually being supplied from the 470 μF capacitor. This is possible since the 5 kHz output pulse train has a duration of only 400 μs in a repetition period of 100 ms.

Single-Channel Infrared Receiver

By comparison, the receiver circuit is more complex since it employs six discrete transistors plus a Darlington pair in addition to three NAND-gates. (See Fig. 12-13.) The detector is a BPW34 photodiode matched to an input impedance of 80 KΩ at 50 kHz. Signals are received in the form of an infrared pulse train from the transmitter. The receiver circuit following the photodiode amplifies, clips, and rectifies the pulse train signal and applies it to a monostable multivibrator which covers the space between two pulse trains. This means that a *dc* voltage is available at the output of the receiver as long as the transmitter signal is held on. This receiver output can be used to operate a relay, simple escapement or a signalling light (e.g., a filament bulb or LED).

Since ambient light will introduce a "noise" voltage or interference in the diode, the circuit is intended for narrow band working which operates by placing an infrared filter in front of the photodiode. This can be an infrared photographic filter, or a section of unexposed but developed color film (e.g., Agfa CT18). The transmitter-receiver combination should then work satisfactorily in ambient light intensities up to 10,000 lux with fluorescent light, 4000 in sunlight, or 500 lux maximum in the case of filament lighting.

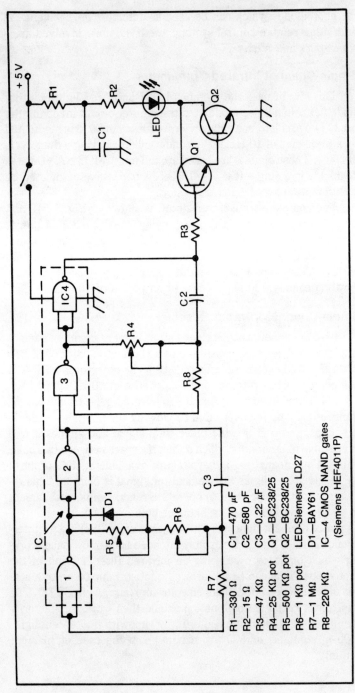

R1—330 Ω
R2—15 Ω
R3—47 KΩ
R4—25 KΩ pot
R5—500 KΩ pot
R6—1 KΩ pot
R7—1 MΩ
R8—220 KΩ

C1—470 μF
C2—580 pF
C3—0.22 μF
Q1—BC238/25
Q2—BC238/25
LED-Siemens LD27
D1—BAY61
IC—4 CMOS NAND gates
(Siemens HEF4011P)

Fig. 12-12. Design for an infrared transmitter by Siemens.

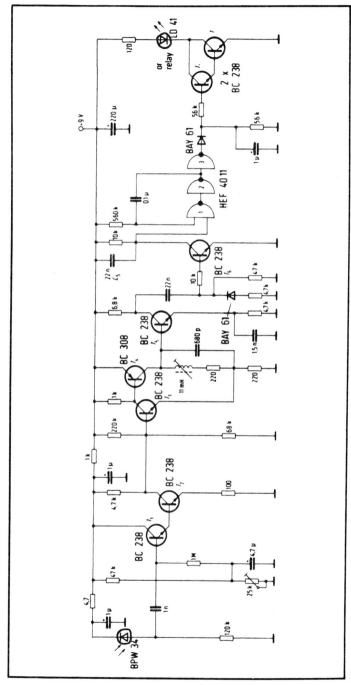

Fig. 12-13. Design for a matching infrared receiver by Siemens.

A simpler receiver circuit is shown in Fig. 12-14 but will only be suitable for working in dull ambient light (less than 500 lux).

ELECTRONIC REV COUNTER

The (Mullard) SAK140 is an integrated circuit designed as a revolution counter for car engines, etc. Connected to the contact breaker, it is fed by input pulses at "engine speed" rate and converts these pulses into output current pulses of constant duration and amplitude. The output pulse duration is determined by an external resistor—capacitor network. By suitable choice of R and C, the pulse "count" can be indicated on any milliammeter. The circuit will also work on any supply voltage between 10 and 18 volts (e.g., from a car's 12-volt battery) and performance is independent of actual supply voltage (or variation in supply voltage).

The complete circuit is shown in Fig. 12-15. Resistor R1 is selected so that the input current does not exceed 10 mA (a suitable value for 12-volts supply is 15 KΩ, when typical input current will be 5 mA). The diode acts as a voltage regulator to prevent overloading by large input pulses.

The peak output current is determined by the value of R2 plus R3. This should be at least 50 Ω, the actual value being chosen to suit the range of the milliammeter used. If R2 is made 50 Ω, then R3 can be made 1 KΩ, say, and adjusted to suit the range of the milliammeter.

The output pulse duration is determined by the combination of R4 and C2. Suitable values can be found by experiment, the suggested starting point being:

R4—270 KΩ
C2—10 nF

QUARTZ CRYSTAL CLOCK

The (Mullard) SAA1114 is a C-MOS integrated circuit designed to work as the "heart" of a crystal controlled clock powered by a single battery. It comprises a master 4 MHz oscillator, a 22-stage frequency divider and a driver for a unipolar stepper motor. With a crystal frequency of 4, 1943 MHz, the output is in the form of a 1 Hz (1 second) pulse of 31.25 milliseconds duration.

A complete clock circuit is shown in 12-16 and requires only a few external components. The quartz crystal is a critical component and is associated with a trimmer capacitor C1 for time adjust-

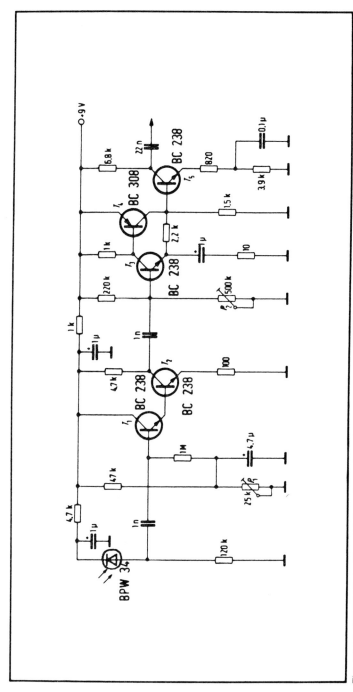

Fig. 12-14. Simpler broad-band infrared receiver circuit.

167

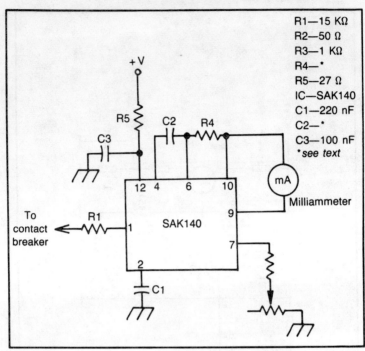

Fig. 12-15. Electronic rev counter circuit using the SAK140IC.

R1—15 KΩ
R2—50 Ω
R3—1 KΩ
R4—*
R5—27 Ω
IC—SAK140
C1—220 nF
C2—*
C3—100 nF
*see text

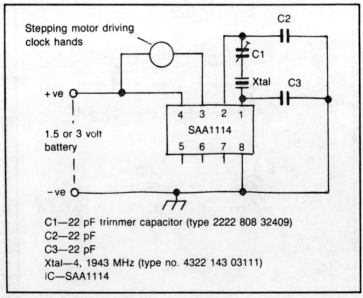

Fig. 12-16. Crystal controlled clock circuit.

C1—22 pF trimmer capacitor (type 2222 808 32409)
C2—22 pF
C3—22 pF
Xtal—4, 1943 MHz (type no. 4322 143 03111)
IC—SAA1114

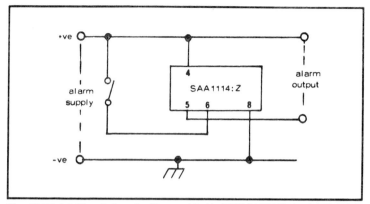

Fig. 12-17. Additional alarm facility provided in ICSAA1114:Z via pins 5 and 6.

ment. Maximum supply voltage is 3 volts, the circuit drawing a current of about 50 A and supplying a motor output current of about 50 mA.

Another version of this particular IC is also available which incorporates an alarm circuit triggered by an alarm switch operated by the clock hand movement. Output of this alarm from pins 5 to 6 is a 250 Hz tone signal operating for 4 seconds when the alarm is triggered. External connections for this alarm circuit are shown in Fig. 12-17, the clock motor circuit being as in Fig. 12-16.

Chapter 13

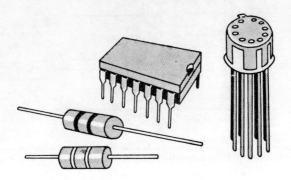

Construction Methods

Many circuits have been presented throughout this book, and there are probably several you would like to build and/or experiment with. Two or more circuits may be combined to create your own custom projects. This final chapter will give you a few tips on constructing electronic projects.

BREADBOARDING

If you are experimenting with a circuit, you want to be able to make solderless connections that can easily be altered. You may have to try several combinations of component values before getting the exact results you want. Soldering, unsoldering and resoldering can be tedious at best. Mistakes can be disastrous. Repeated solderings increase the chances of cold solder joints and unreliable connections. Even more importantly, some components (especially semiconductors like integrated circuits) can be ruined by excessive heat.

Fortunately, there is a much more practical way to set up temporary circuits—the breadboard. In its simplest form, this is merely a solderless socket that the various component leads and wires can quickly be plugged into or pulled out of. The various holes in this type of socket are electrically interconnected. The most commonly used interconnection pattern is illustrated in Fig. 13-1.

While solderless sockets of this type are inexpensive and readily available, there may be times when you will prefer to create your

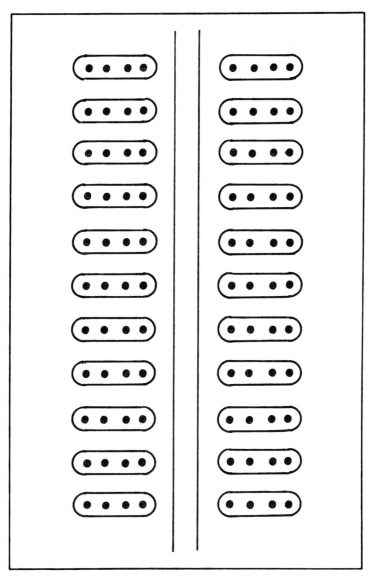

Fig. 13-1. A solderless socket is used for temporary construction of circuits.

own customized solderless socket with Fahrnstock clips, as shown in Fig. 13-2. Interconnections are made between the clips with ordinary hook-up wire. This type of home-brew breadboard may be necessary when large or unusually shaped components, which won't fit in a standard solderless socket, are used.

171

A solderless socket can make experimentation and circuit design much easier, but it is even more useful as part of a complete breadboarding system. A typical system of this type is shown in Fig. 13-3.

These breadboarding systems consist of a solderless socket and various commonly used sub-circuits, such as power supplies and oscillators. These sub-circuits can be separate, stand-alone modules used along with a simple solderless socket, but it is generally more convenient to have them grouped together within a single, compact unit, as shown in the photo. In either case, these sub-circuits will be needed far too often to make breadboarding them from scratch each time they're needed reasonable. Frequently employed sub-circuits should be permanently constructed.

Most breadboarding systems also have one or more potentiometers and switches available for convenient use in experimental circuits.

Remember to make all changes with the power off to reduce the risk of damaging some components (especially ICs and other semiconductors) or, in some cases, suffering severe injury yourself. Bear in mind at all times that electrical shocks can be very painful, or even fatal—always use caution.

Some circuits might not work well (or at all) in a standard solderless breadboard. This is usually true in high frequency circuits where the length of connecting wires, "phantom" components (especially inductances and capacitances) and shielding (or lack thereof) can become critical. Fortunately, the circuit which can not be prototyped in a breadboard socket is very much the exception

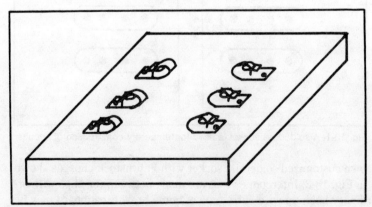

Fig. 13-2. You can create your own customized solderless socket with Fahrnstock clips.

Fig. 13-3. A breadboarding system consists of a solderless socket and standard, commonly used sub-circuits.

to the rule. If high frequencies are involved in the circuit you are working with, keep interconnecting wires as short as possible. If the circuit operates incorrectly or erratically, try relocating some of the components.

Somewhat more common are circuits which may change their operating parameters noticeably when a more permanent type of connection is used. Be aware of this potential problem. There really isn't much you can do about it in advance, but at least you can be prepared to recognize such problems when they do crop up. At least, you'll be able to save a lot of time and hair pulling.

PERMANENT CONSTRUCTION METHODS

Once you have designed your circuit, breadboarded the project, and gotten all of the bugs out, you will probably want to rebuild some circuits in a more permanent way. Solderless breadboarding sockets are great for testing and experimenting with prototype circuits, but they really aren't much good when it comes to putting the circuit to practical use.

Breadboarded circuits, by definition, have nonpermanent connections. In actual use, some component leads may bend and touch each other, creating potentially harmful shorts. Components may even fall out of the socket altogether when the device is moved about. Interference signals can easily be generated and picked up by the exposed wiring.

173

Generally, packaging a circuit built on a solderless socket will be tricky at best. They tend not to fit very well in standard circuit housings and boxes. Besides, a solderless socket is fairly expensive. It is certainly worth the price if it is re-used for many different circuits. But if you tie it up with a single permanent circuit, you're only cheating yourself. Less expensive methods that are more reliable, more compact, and that offer better overall performance are readily available.

Some relatively simple circuits can be constructed on a perforated circuit board, with component leads and jumper wires soldered directly together, using point to point wiring. Only very, very small, very simple circuits should ever be wired directly together without any supporting circuit board. Otherwise you will end up with a "rat's nest" of jumbled wiring that is next to impossible to trace if an error is made, or if the circuit needs to be serviced or modified at a later date. In addition, a lot of loose hanging wires can create their own problems, such as stray capacitances and inductances between them, allowing signals to get into the wrong portions of the circuit.

"Rat's nest" wiring is also just begging for internal breaks within the wires, and short circuits between them. Momentary, intermittent shorts may not cause permanent damage in all cases, but they can result in some strange circuit performance that can be maddeningly frustrating to diagnose and service.

Symptoms of "rat's nest" wiring can also be a problem with some complex circuits on perf boards. Always try to minimize crossings of jumper wires. Use straight line paths for jumper wires whenever possible. The circuit should be laid out for the minimum possible number of jumpers. Some will probably be unavoidable, but limit them whenever possible.

You should also try to position all of the components on the board to see how they'll fit before you even plug in your soldering iron. This will help you avoid unpleasant surprises, like ending up with no place to put that big filter capacitor.

For moderate to complex circuits, or for circuits from which a number of duplicates will be built, a printed circuit board gives very good results. Copper traces on one side (or, in very complex circuits, on both sides) of the board act as connecting wires between the components. Very steady, stable, and sturdy connections can be made, since the component leads are soldered directly to the supporting board itself.

174

Great care must be taken in laying out a PC board to eliminate wire crossings. Traces cannot cross each other. If a crossing is absolutely essential, a wire jumper must be used.

Stray capacitances between traces can adversely affect circuit performance. In critical circuits, a guard band between traces can help reduce the potential problem.

Especially in circuits using ICs, the copper traces are usually placed very close to each other. This means a short circuit is very easy to create. A small speck of solder, or a piece of a component's excess lead could easily bridge across two adjacent traces, creating a short. Only small amounts of solder should be used. Too much will flow and bridge across adjacent traces.

Tiny, near invisible hairline cracks in the copper traces can also be problematic, if you're not careful. Generally, fairly wide traces that are widely spaced are the easiest to work with. However, this isn't always practical with all circuits—especially where ICs are used.

A printed circuit board type of construction results in very short component leads. Lengthy leads aren't needed. This can help minimize interference and stray capacitance problems.

More and more circuits being constructed today use the wire-wrapping method. A thin wire is wrapped tightly around a square post. The edges of the post bite into the wire, making a good electrical and physical connection without soldering. Components are fitted into special sockets that connect their leads to the square wrapping posts. This form of construction is most appropriate for circuits made up primarily of a number of integrated circuits.If just a few discrete components are used, they can be fitted into special sockets, or soldered directly, while the connections to the ICs are wire-wrapped (hybrid construction). In circuits involving many discrete components, the wire-wrapping method tends to be rather impractical.

Wire-wrapped connections can be made (or unmade) quickly and easily, without risking potential heat damage to delicate semiconductor components.

There are some disadvantages to this type of construction. Discrete components are awkward at best. The thin wire-wrapping wire is very fragile, and easily broken. It can only carry very low power signals. The wiring can be very difficult to trace.

Still, when many ICs are involved (some circuits require several dozen), wire-wrapping is a very convenient form of construction.

SOCKETS

People working in electronics disagree strongly about the use of IC sockets. Some technicians say sockets should only be used for chips that are frequently changed (such as ROMs containing different programming), or possibly for very expensive ICs. Others (myself included) recommend the regular use of sockets on all ICs.

It may seem silly to protect a 25¢ IC with a 50¢ socket, but what you are really protecting is your own time and sanity. If you make a mistake, or if an IC has to be replaced for servicing, you will have to desolder and resolder each individual pin, watching out for solder bridges and over-heating. Frankly, I don't think it's worth the trouble. Sockets don't add that much to the cost of a project, and they can head off a lot of grief and frustration if problems do arise. Think of them as sort of an insurance policy.

There are some cases in which sockets are undesirable. In equipment for field use which is likely to be bounced around a lot, direct soldering may be desirable, to prevent a chip's pins from being bounced out of place.

A few (very few) high frequency circuits can be disturbed by the slightly poorer electrical connection of a socket. But these are few and far between. In 99% of the circuits you'll work with, using IC sockets will cause no problems and could save you from a lot of needless hassle.

HEAT SINKS

Where integrated circuits handle moderate powers and a heat sink is necessary to dissipate heat generated within the IC itself, areas etched on the copper of a printed circuit board can conveniently be used as heat sinks. ICs which are suitable for heat sinks of this type are usually fitted with a tab or tabs for soldering directly to the copper bands forming the heat sink.

The area of copper needed for a heat sink can be calculated quite simply, knowing the relevant circuit parameters. First it is necessary to determine the maximum power to be dissipated, using the formula:

$$\text{Power (watts)} = 0.4 \frac{V_s^2}{8R_L} + V_s \bullet I_d$$

where V_s is the maximum supply voltage
I_d is the quiescent drain current in amps under the

most adverse conditions.

R_L is the load resistance (e.g., the loudspeaker resistance in the case of an audio amplifier circuit).

Strictly speaking the value of V_s used should be the battery voltage plus an additional 10 percent, e.g., if the circuit is powered by a 12-volt battery, the value of V_s to use in the formula is 12 + 1.2 = 13.2 volts. This allows for possible fluctuations in power level, such as when using a new battery. If the circuit has a stabilized power supply, then V_s can be taken as this supply voltage.

The quiescent drain current (I_d) is found from the IC parameters as specified by the manufacturers and will be dependent on supply voltage. Figures may be quoted for "typical" and "maximum." In this case, use the maximum values.

Figure 13-4 then gives the relationship between power to be dissipated and copper area, based on a maximum ambient temperature of 55 °C (which is a safe limit for most IC devices).

Example: Supply voltage for a particular Ic is 12 volts. Load resistance if 4 Ω and the maximum quiescent current drain quoted for the IC at this operating voltage is 20 milliamps. The supply volt-

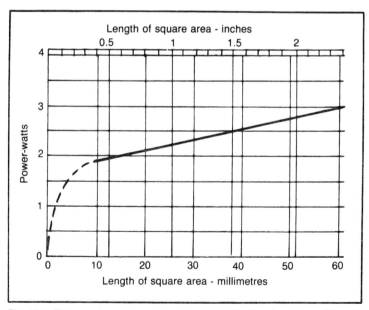

Fig. 13-4. This graph can be used to determine the size of squares of copper required for heat sinks on printed circuit boards. Size is given as length of a square. Any other shape of the same area can be used (see text).

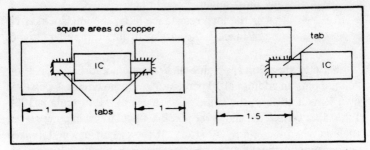

Fig. 13-5. Copper area determined from Fig. 13-4 is for two equal squares (one at each end of the IC). If a single square is used at one end of the IC, its area needs to be slightly greater for the same heat dissipation.

age is not stabilized, so the value to use for V_s is

$$12 + 1.2 = 13.2 \text{ volts}$$

$$\text{Thus power} = 0.4 \times \frac{13.2^2}{8 \times 4} + (13.2 \times 0.020)$$

$$= 2.178 + 0.264$$

$$= 2.422 \text{ watts (say 2.5 watts)}$$

From Fig. 13-4, a suitable copper area is seen to be a 40 mm square.

This heat sink area can be arranged in two squares (if the IC has two tags); or a single square (if the IC has one tag) (see Fig. 13-5). Of course, the area does not have to be a square. This is simply the easiest shape to calculate. It can be rectangular, regular or irregular in shape, provided there is sufficient area. A point to be borne in mind, however, is that with any shape the copper area nearest the tag will have greater efficiency as a heat dissipator, so shapes which concentrate the area in this region are better than those that do not (see Fig. 13-6). If such a shape cannot be incorporated conveniently on the printed circuit layout, and a less efficient shape has to be used, then it may be necessary to increase the actual area of copper to compensate. Copper areas given in Fig. 5-1 should be adequate since most ICs can be worked at fairly ambient temperatures without trouble (e.g., up to 70 °C). Very approximately this higher temperature operation will be provided by a copper area of a little more than one half that given by the graph, so there is a fair margin for error available when using this graph.

The graph also shows that the area of copper necessary to dis-

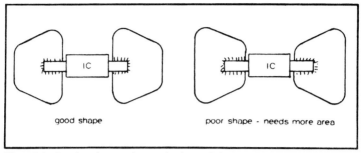

Fig. 13-6. Good and poor shapes for heat sink areas on PCBs.

sipate powers of 3 watts or more tends to become excessive, compared with the area of printed circuit panel actually required for the circuit itself. Where higher powers have to be dissipated, therefore, it is usually more convenient (and more efficient) to dissipate heat by an external heat sink fitted to the IC itself. Some examples of external heat sinks are shown in Fig. 13-7.

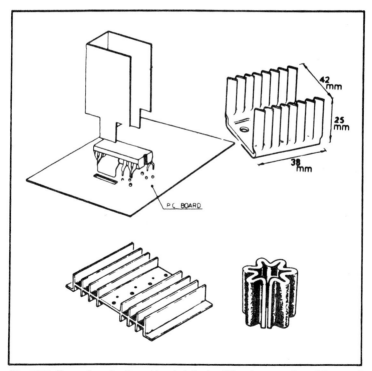

Fig. 13-7. Examples of external heat sinks for fitting to power transistors and integrated circuits.

179

Index

Edited by Carl D. Aron

Other Bestsellers From TAB

☐ **THE LINEAR IC HANDBOOK—Morley**

Far more than a replacement for manufacturers' data books. *The Linear IC Handbook* covers linear IC offerings from all the major manufacturers—complete with specifications, data sheet parameters, and price information—along with technological background on linear ICs. It gives you instant access to data on how linear ICs are fabricated, how they work, what types are available, and techniques for designing them. 624 pp., 366 illus. 6″ × 9″.
Hard $49.50   Book No. 2672

☐ **THE 555 IC PROJECT BOOK—Traister**

Now, with this exceptionally well-documented project guide, you can begin to use the 555 timer IC in a variety of useful projects that are both easy and fun to put together. From an IC metronome to a ten-second timer and even an electronic organ, this is an exciting collection of 33 different projects that even a novice at electronics can make easily, inexpensively, and in only a few hours time. Most important it provides the know-how to start you designing your own original 555 IC projects to suit your own special needs. 224 pp., 110 illus.
**Paper $11.95   Hard $18.95
Book No. 1996**

☐ **THE ENCYCLOPEDIA OF ELECTRONIC CIRCUITS—Graf**

Here's the electronics hobbyist's and technician's dream treasury of analog and digital circuits—nearly 100 circuit categories . . . over 1,200 individual circuits designed for long-lasting applications potential. Adding even more to the value of this resource is the exhaustively thorough index which gives you instant access to exactly the circuits you need each and every time! 768 pp., 1,782 illus. 7″ × 10″.
Paper $29.95   Book No. 1938

☐ **BASIC INTEGRATED CIRCUITS—Marks**

With the step-by-step guidance provided by electronics design expert Myles Marks, anyone with basic electronics know-how can design and build almost any type of modern IC device for almost any application imaginable! In fact, this is the ideal sourcebook for every hobbyist or experimenter who wants to expand his digital electronics knowledge and begin exploring the fascinating new possibilities offered by today's IC technology. 432 pp., 319 illus.
**Paper $16.95   Hard $26.95
Book No. 2609**

☐ **101 SOUND, LIGHT AND POWER IC PROJECT—Shoemaker**

At last! Here's an IC project guide that doesn't stop with how and why ICs function . . . it goes one step further to give you hands-on experience in the interfacing of integrated circuits to solve real-world problems. Projects include sound control circuits such as alarms and intercoms; light control projects from photoflash slave to a monitor/alarm; power control units and much more! 384 pp., 135 illus.
**Paper $16.95   Hard $24.95
Book No. 2604**

☐ **DESIGNING IC CIRCUITS . . . WITH EXPERIMENTS—Horn**

With this excellent sourcebook as your guide, you'll be able to get started in the designing of your own practical circuits using op amps, 555 timers, voltage regulators, linear ICs, digital ICs, and other commonly available IC devices. It's crammed with practical design and construction tips and hints that are guaranteed to save you time, effort, and frustration no matter what your IC application needs. 364 pp., 397 illus.
**Paper $16.95   Hard $24.95
Book No. 1925**

Other Bestsellers From TAB

[ ] **TRANSISTOR CIRCUIT DESIGN—with Experiments —Horn**

Here it is! The electronics project guide that you've been asking for: a practical introduction to transistor circuit design and construction! Exceptionally easy-to-follow and overflowing with unique and practical projects complete with detailed circuit descriptions and schematics diagrams. Hobbyists and experimenters will find it especially valuable for its wealth of example circuits and project plans and it's an essential guide for anyone who wants to fully understand the design and applications potential of transistor circuitry! 434 pp., 286 illus.
Paper $14.95   Book No. 1875

[ ] **THE MASTER IC COOKBOOK—Hallmark**

"Use-it-now" data on *every* IC family and function—CMOS and TTL 4000- and 7400-series digital ICs, exotic CMOS, and linear ICs! It's a ONE-STOP SOURCE of descriptions, pinouts, and absolute maximum ratings for *all* classifications of ICs. Covers logic diagrams, power dissipation, propagation delay time (or maximum clock frequency for flip-flops, counters, and registers), truth tables and more! Includes IC circuits you can build! 476 pp., 742 illus.
Paper $16.95   Book No. 1199

[ ] **BASIC INTEGRATED CIRCUIT THEORY AND PROJECTS—Adams**

Here's the ideal guide for anyone who wnats to learn how integrated circuits work and who wants to begin using both analog and digital ICs in practical, working applications! Absolutely no advanced math or science background is needed, because the author has broken down IC theory into easily digestible segments, complete with applications data and 24 useful projects that provide you with hands-on use experience. You can build a NAND gate, series NAND gates, a wired AND gate, a NOR gate, or a LM324 op amp amplifier. 266 pp., 295 illus.
Paper $11.95   Book No. 1699

[ ] **MASTER HANDBOOK OF 1001 PRACTICAL ELECTRONIC CIRCUITS**

The ideal schematic sourcebook of IC and transistor circuits for practically anything and everything—with ALL the data needed to put them to work . . . each circuit diagram has *every* component carefully labeled, and *every* schematic has all the facts you need to construct exactly the type of circuit you need! Includes an ultra-complete 22-page index, plus appendix of IC substitutions. 602 pp., over 1,250 illus.
Paper $19.95   Book No. 800